TUTOR DELIVERY PACK
MATHEMATICS
— GCSE —
HIGHER

Author: Catherine Murphy

CONTENTS

MATHS
— HIGHER —

Edexcel

Contents

HOW TO USE THIS PACK

The *Tutors' Guild* Maths Tutor Delivery Pack gives you all of the tools you need to deliver effective Maths lessons to Edexcel GCSE (9–1) students who are sitting the Higher paper. Everything in this pack is available for you to download as an editable file. This means that every lesson can be edited to suit the needs of your student, but also that you can print off each resource as many times as you need.

LESSONS

There are 38 one-hour, six-page lessons in this Tutor Delivery Pack. Most tutors working for a full year will have around 38 lessons with a student. If you have less contact time, you can choose which lessons are most important to the student and build your own course, using the customisable digital version of this pack. Each lesson is standalone and can be taught independently from those preceding it.

If you have more than 38 lessons together, or your lessons are longer than one hour, you can incorporate assessment from the accompanying Tutor Assessment Pack (ISBN: 9781292195780). There is an *end-of-topic test* for every lesson in this pack, as well as *checkpoint challenges* and *practice papers*. All of the papers can also be given as homework, used as diagnostic tests or incorporated into revision.

LESSON PLANS

The first page of each lesson is your *lesson plan*. It is designed specifically for tutors and is intended to guide you through a one-hour session in either a one-to-one or small group setting. It is not designed to be student-facing.

LEARNING OBJECTIVES AND SPECIFICATION LINKS

At the top of each lesson plan, you will find two lists. The first – *learning objectives* – is a list of your aims for the lesson. The learning objectives will be informed by the specification but may have been rephrased to make sure they are accessible to and useful for everyone. You can discuss these with the student or use them for your own reference when tracking progress. The second list – *specification links* – shows you where in the specification you can find the objectives relevant to the lesson. You can find out more about the specification on pages 7–10.

ACTIVITIES

The first five minutes of your lesson should be spent reviewing the previous week's homework. You should not mark the homework during contact time: instead, use the time to talk through what the student learned and enjoyed, and any difficulties they encountered.

The final five minutes should be used to set homework for the forthcoming week. There are three ways to do this: using the *end-of-lesson report* on page 16; orally with a parent or guardian; or simply using the *homework activity sheet* on the fifth page of each lesson.

In each lesson plan, you will find four types of activities:
- *starter activities* are 5–10 minutes each and provide an introduction to the topic
- *main activities* are up to 40 minutes long and are more involved, focussing on the main objectives of the lesson
- *plenary activities* are 5–10 minutes each, require little to no writing and recap the main learning points or prepare for the homework
- *homework activities* can be up to an hour long and put learning into practice.

In the lesson plan, you will find a page reference (where the activity is paper-based), a suggested timeframe and teaching notes for each activity. The teaching notes will help to guide you in delivering the activity and will also advise you on any common misconceptions associated with the topic.

HOW TO USE THIS PACK

SUPPORT AND EXTENSION IDEAS

This pack is aimed at students who are targeted grades 4–9, but every student is different: some will struggle with activities that others working at the same level find straightforward. In these sections, you will find ideas for providing some differentiation throughout the activities.

PROGRESS AND OBSERVATIONS

This section is left blank for you to use as appropriate. You can then use the notes you make to inform assessment and future lessons, as well as to inform *progress reports* to parents.

ACTIVITY SHEETS

There are four student-facing *activity sheets* for each lesson: one for the starter activities; two for main activities and one for the homework activity. On each sheet, you'll find activity-specific lesson objectives, an equipment list and a suggested timeframe. All activities are phrased for one-to-one tutoring but are equally as appropriate for small group settings. If you have a small group and the task asks you to work in pairs or challenge each other, ask the students to pair up while you observe and offer advice as necessary. Where appropriate, answers can be found on the sixth page of the lesson.

DIAGNOSTICS

The first lesson in this pack is a diagnostic lesson, designed to help you find out more about your student: their likes and dislikes; strengths and weaknesses; and personality traits. As well as the diagnostic lesson, the *needs analysis* section (pages 13–14) allows you, the student and the student's parents to investigate together which areas of the subject will need greater focus. Together, these sections will help you deliver the most effective, best value tuition.

PROGRESS REPORT

This can be used to inform parents or for your own planning as frequently or infrequently as is useful for you. Spend some time discussing the statements on the report with the student. Be prepared, though – some students will tell you there isn't anything that they enjoy about the subject!

END-OF-LESSON REPORT

Parent participation will vary greatly. The *end-of-lesson* report is useful for efficiently feeding back to parents who prefer an update after each lesson. There is space to review completed homework and achievements in the lesson, as well as space for the student to explain how confident they feel after the lesson. Finally, there is a section on what steps, including homework, the parent and student can take to consolidate learning or prepare for the following week. The *end-of-lesson* report may also be useful for communicating with some parents who speak English as a second language, as written information may be easier to follow.

CERTIFICATES

In the digital version of this pack, you will find two customisable certificates. These can be edited to celebrate achievements of any size.

PEARSON PROGRESSION SCALE

 Each question in this pack features a Step icon that indicates the level of challenge aligned to the Pearson Progression Map and Scale. To find out more about the Progression Scale for Maths and to see how it relates to indicative GCSE 9–1 grades go to www.pearsonschools.co.uk/ProgressionServices

INFORMATION FOR PARENTS AND GUARDIANS

INTRODUCTION

Your child's tutor will often make use of resources from the *Tutors' Guild* series. These resources have been written especially for the new GCSE (9–1) qualifications and are tailored to the Edexcel GCSE (9–1) Mathematics specification. The tutor will use their expert knowledge and judgement to assess the student's current needs. This will allow them to target areas for improvement, build confidence levels and develop skills as quickly as possible to ensure the best chance of success.

Just as a classroom teacher might do, the tutor will use lesson plans and activities designed to prepare the student for the GCSE (9–1) exams. Each set of resources has been designed by experts in GCSE (9–1) Mathematics and reviewed by tutors to ensure it offers great quality, effective and engaging teaching. All *Tutors' Guild* resources are flexible and fully adaptable, so you can be confident that the tuition your child receives is tailored to his or her needs.

GETTING STARTED

Before tuition can begin, the tutor will need to know more about your motives for employing them in order to set clear, achievable goals. They will also try to learn more about the student to ensure lessons are as useful and engaging as possible.

To gather this information, the tutor will work through the *needs analysis* pages of this pack with you. It shouldn't take too long, but it will really maximise the value of the tuition time you pay for. You could also take this opportunity to discuss with the tutor any questions or concerns you may have.

LESSONS AND HOMEWORK

Each lesson will have the same structure: there will be a starter, which is a quick introduction to the topic; some main activities, which will look at the topic in greater detail; and a plenary activity, which will be used to round off the topic. Throughout the year, the student will become increasingly confident with the content of the specification, but will also improve his or her numerical fluency, problem solving skills and multiplicative reasoning through a carefully balanced range of activities.

At the end of each lesson, your tutor will set some homework, which should take no longer than an hour to complete. If you don't want the tutor to set homework, please let them know. If you are happy for homework to be given, the tutor will either discuss the homework task with you at the end of the lesson or give you an end-of-lesson report. All of the homework activities are designed to be completed independently but if you would like to help with completion of homework, your tutor will be able to tell you how you can help.

FURTHER SUPPORT

Parents and guardians often ask a tutor what else they can do to support learning or what resources they can buy to provide extra revision and practice. As a Pearson resource, *Tutors' Guild* has been designed to complement the popular *Revise* series. Useful titles you may wish to purchase include:

- *Revise* Edexcel GCSE (9–1) Mathematics Higher Revision Guide (ISBN: 9781447988090)
- *Revise* Edexcel GCSE (9–1) Mathematics Higher Revision Workbook (ISBN: 9781292210889)
- *Revise* Edexcel GCSE (9–1) Mathematics Higher Revision Cards (ISBN: 9781292173221)
- *Revise* Edexcel GCSE (9–1) Mathematics Higher Practice Papers Plus[+] (ISBN: 9781292096315)

Using pages 11–12 of this pack, your tutor will be able to tell you which pages of the *Revise* resources are appropriate for each lesson. If you purchase a set of Revision Cards, each card has a page reference in the top corner.

MATHS
— HIGHER —

INFORMATION FOR PARENTS AND GUARDIANS

WHAT'S IN THE TEST?

You may have heard a lot about the new GCSE (9–1) qualifications from your child's school, from other parents or in the media. Here is a breakdown of the Edexcel GCSE (9–1) Mathematics exams.

THE PAPERS

Your child will sit three GCSE (9–1) Mathematics papers. The exam is tiered, which means all candidates sit either Foundation or Higher papers. Each paper is worth 80 marks – one third of the total marks available. Candidates are given 1 hour and 30 minutes to complete each paper.

Paper 1 is non-calculator, while calculators are allowed in Papers 2 and 3. The GCSE (9–1) qualifications see an increase in the amount of calculator-allowed assessment, from 50% to 66.6%.

ASSESSMENT OBJECTIVES

There are three broad types of skills that are tested in the exams. Each one has its own *Assessment Objective*.

Assessment Objective 1 (AO1) tests how well a candidate can apply standard techniques. AO1 is the most accessible objective for the majority of candidates and could test a range of content areas, from ordering decimals, fractions and percentages to calculating with roots and powers. Around 50% of the marks available on Foundation papers and 40% of the marks available on Higher papers are awarded for AO1.

Assessment Objective 2 (AO2) assesses reasoning, interpretation and communication in Mathematics. It involves making inferences and conclusions, presenting evidence and proving answers. Trialling of the new exams found that many candidates find AO2 difficult to access. AO2 accounts for 25% of the Foundation marks and 30% of the Higher marks.

Assessment Objective 3 (AO3) assesses problem-solving skills. Based on recent trials of the new exams, this seems to be the area that causes candidates the most difficulty. However, mastering problem-solving could prove hugely beneficial, as it is worth 25% of the total marks for Foundation students and 30% for Higher students. The GCSE (9–1) Mathematics area of the Edexcel website has a range of free resources to help strengthen these skills.

RESULTS AND GRADES

GCSE results day is typically the third or fourth Thursday in August. It is the same day across the country, so you can find out the exact date online. On results day, the student will be given a slip of paper (or one per exam board, if the school hasn't collated them) with an overall grade for each GCSE. Grades for the GCSE qualifications are no longer given as letters (A*–U) but as numbers (9–1) instead. The diagram below shows roughly how the old-style grades translate to the new ones.

Previous grade	A*		A	B		C	D	E	F	G	U
New grade	9	8	7	6	5	4	3	2	1		U

As you can see, the new grade 9 is pitched higher than an A*. There is a wider spread of grades available for students whose target would previously have been a B/C. Because Mathematics is tiered, Foundation students will be able to access grades 1–5, whereas Higher students should be aiming to achieve grades 4–9.

SPECIFICATION GUIDANCE

The new Edexcel GCSE (9–1) Mathematics specification was introduced in 2015, with first assessment in 2017. If you have experience in tutoring or teaching the previous curriculum, much of the content and assessment will be familiar. If this is the case, please turn to pages 8–10 for guidance on what has changed.

If you are new to tutoring GCSE (9–1) Mathematics, this page will give you a brief introduction before you move on to pages 8–10. Further guidance on specific areas of the specification – including common misconceptions and barriers to learning – can be found in the lesson plans throughout this book. The complete specification can be found on the Edexcel website.

KEY FACTS
Content domains
There are six areas of mathematics that will be assessed:
1. Number
2. Algebra
3. Ratio, proportion and rates of change
4. Geometry and measures
5. Probability*
6. Statistics*

The weighting of these content domains will be approximately as follows.

Content domain	Foundation	Higher
Number	25%	15%
Algebra	20%	30%
Ratio, proportion and rates of change	25%	20%
Geometry and measures	15%	20%
Statistics and probability*	15%	15%

*Statistics and probability are often considered together in assessment weightings.

The six domains are further broken down into smaller content areas. These are set out from page 5 onwards of the Edexcel specification, which can be found on Edexcel's website. Foundation students will need to know all of the content identified in the specification in standard type, as well as the content in underlined type. Underlined content will push Foundation students a little further. Higher students will be tested on the areas in standard type, underlined type and **bold type**.

Each lesson plan in this pack highlights which areas of the specification are covered. In order to maximise your student's chances of success, the pack covers the most important specification areas and those students struggle with the most; it is intended to supplement and enhance classroom teaching and does not therefore cover the entire specification.

Exam papers
Both Foundation and Higher students will sit three exam papers:
- Paper 1; non-calculator; 80 marks; 1.5 hours
- Paper 2; calculator; 80 marks; 1.5 hours
- Paper 3; calculator; 80 marks; 1.5 hours

The six content domains will be assessed on all three of the papers. As the breakdown above shows, each exam paper is given an equal weighting: one third of the total available marks is available for each paper.

Foundation students will be able to access grades 1–5 and Higher students will be able to access grades 4–9.
You will find further information about the format and structure of the exams and the new grading system in the corresponding *Assessment Pack* for this title (ISBN: 9781292195780).

WHAT'S CHANGED?

Key changes

There are several key changes to the Edexcel GCSE (9–1) Mathematics course, brought about by new Ofqual requirements. The hope is that increasing the demand of GCSE Mathematics will better prepare students to apply their learning in everyday life, in work and in further studies. The new course will be more demanding in the following ways.

- **There is more subject content.**
  You'll have more topics to cover with your student, and the topics will be denser. This will change how you teach the course: will you recommend increased contact time, set more independent work or prioritise which content you cover?
- **Content is more demanding.**
  Both Foundation and Higher students will face more difficult topics than before.
- **Students will need to memorise more formulae.**
  Fewer formulae will be available to students in the exams. The formulae needed can be found on page 10.
- **There are more questions covering difficult skills.**
  Assessment objectives testing problem solving and reasoning carry more marks than previously for both Foundation and Higher students. These skills present difficulties for many students.
- **There are more marks to be gained for more difficult questions.**
  For both Foundation and Higher students, fewer marks will be available for lower-grade questions and more marks will be attributed to the questions at the top end of the grade scale.
- **Total exam time has increased.**
  There are now three exam papers to sit rather than the previous two, taking total exam time from 3.5 hours to 4.5 hours. This may present additional problems for students with low attention or concentration levels.

New content

For Foundation students, there is a large number of new topics that, in the previous GCSE specification, were Higher tier only. New topics include the following:

- compound interest and reverse percentages
- direct and indirect proportion
- standard form.

If you exclusively teach Foundation students, it may have been a while since you have come across this content and, as such, you may wish to spend some time refamiliarising yourself with it before tuition begins.

For Higher students, there are some new topics at the top end of the grade scale. These are intended to stretch students who go on to study A level. Such topics include the following:

- expanding the products or more than two binomials
- calculating or estimating gradients of graphs and areas under graphs, and interpreting results in real-life cases
- deducing turning points by completing the square.

To make way for this new content, some previously covered topics have been omitted from the new specification, including: 3D co-ordinates, imperial units of measure, and tessellations.

While this pack will help you to deliver the new content, you should make sure you are familiar and comfortable with the new topics and best practices for teaching them.

A full list of new content can be found on Edexcel's website.

REASONING AND PROBLEM-SOLVING SKILLS

The new GCSE (9–1) qualification places increased emphasis on the more involved skills of reasoning and problem-solving than previously, so you need to make sure you are able to help your students develop such skills.

Reasoning, interpreting and communication mathematically

These skills are covered by the Assessment Objective AO2. Edexcel's trials have found that students could generally benefit from more practice of this Assessment Objective, which covers skills such as making deductions and inferences, drawing conclusions, assessing the validity of an argument and interpreting information. Quality of Written Communication (QWC) is also assessed within AO2. There are no longer marks allocated to QWC, but it is taken into account when considering the effectiveness of a candidate's communication skills.

Questions that will help you to assess your student's reasoning ability will use commands such as *show that* and will involve setting out working in a clear, methodical way. It is worth reinforcing to your student that, in Maths, communicating well and explaining how you've arrived at a solution doesn't mean writing long paragraphs or even full sentences – it's about clear and methodical working, supported by short passages of text where necessary.

Linked to this is the requirement to be able to present arguments effectively or assess the validity of a given argument. Questions testing this skill come in various forms: students may, for example, need to explain why a statement is wrong or answer a question and then provide supporting evidence. Students will often struggle to know what an adequate response to such questions will be, so your support here will be valuable. You could look at acceptable responses in mark schemes or exemplar material with your student, or simply to work through questions orally so that you can guide their response.

Students may also be required to evaluate the presentation of information, such as a chart or table. Perhaps the most useful preparation here is to emphasise best practice in your student's own work and encourage the review of work with a critical eye.

To assess your student's ability to interpret information accurately, you can use questions that rely on the use and manipulation of geometric and graphical information. For example, a question that asks your student to calculate a value for the mean from a frequency table requires a solid understanding of the data that are presented (are they looking at cumulative or grouped frequency, for example?) and how that data should be interpreted to find the correct value.

Problem-solving

The proportion of marks awarded to problem-solving questions has been increased for the GCSE (9–1) qualifications. Previously, both Foundation and Higher exams awarded between 15% and 25% of marks for problem-solving, which is referred to as AO3 in the specification. For the GCSE (9–1) qualifications, Foundation and Higher papers carry approximately 25% and 30% AO3 marks respectively.

Trials have found that, in general, problem-solving is the area of Maths that students find the most difficult. For many, this will be because problem-solving questions often require a different approach from most other mathematical questions: Edexcel refer to such problems as 'non-routine'. The skills that make up AO3 include the following:

- **translating problems from mathematical or non-mathematical contexts into a mathematical process**
  This essentially means taking a problem and working out what maths needs to be done to solve it.
- **making and utilising connections between different mathematical topics**
  For example, recognising that algebra can help to solve probability problems and being able to put that into practice.
- **contextual interpretation of results**
  For example, the logical application of units to an answer or calculation, or appropriate rounding of an answer to account for context (generally, a decimal answer to *What is the capacity of the stadium?* would be inappropriate).
- **evaluation of methods used, results obtained and the effect any assumptions may have had**
  This could involve assessing the effectiveness or accuracy of two different methods, or commenting on the effect on a solution of not having access to complete information.

There are clear steps you can follow with your student to help them gain confidence in problem-solving: first, ensure they understand the problem; then, help them to formulate a plan; then, they can carefully carry out that plan; finally, they should check their answer logically and mathematically.

REQUIRED FORMULAE

Foundation students need to know the following:

Area
rectangle = $l \times w$ parallelogram = $b \times h$

triangle = $\frac{1}{2}b \times h$ trapezium = $\frac{1}{2}(a+b)h$

Volumes
cuboid = $l \times w \times h$ cylinder = $\pi r^2 h$

prism = area of cross section × length

Circles
circumference = π × diameter $C = \pi d$

circumference = 2 × π × radius $C = 2\pi r$

area of circle = π × radius squared $A = \pi r^2$

Compound measures
speed = $\dfrac{\text{distance}}{\text{time}}$ density = $\dfrac{\text{mass}}{\text{volume}}$

The formula for pressure will be provided if relevant.

Pythagoras
Pythagoras' Theorem: for a right-angled triangle, $a^2 + b^2 = c^2$

trigonometric ratios:

$\sin x = \dfrac{\text{opp}}{\text{hyp}}$ $\cos x = \dfrac{\text{adj}}{\text{hyp}}$ $\tan x = \dfrac{\text{opp}}{\text{adj}}$

Higher students need to know the following:

Area
rectangle = $l \times w$ parallelogram = $b \times h$

triangle = $\frac{1}{2}b \times h$ trapezium = $\frac{1}{2}(a+b)h$

Volumes
cuboid = $l \times w \times h$ cylinder = $\pi r^2 h$

prism = area of cross section × length

pyramid = $\dfrac{1}{3}$ × area of base × h

Circles
circumference = π × diameter $C = \pi d$

circumference = 2 × π × radius $C = 2\pi r$

area of circle = π × radius squared $A = \pi r^2$

Compound measures
speed = $\dfrac{\text{distance}}{\text{time}}$ density = $\dfrac{\text{mass}}{\text{volume}}$

The formula for pressure will be provided if relevant.

Pythagoras
Pythagoras' Theorem: for a right-angled triangle, $a^2 + b^2 = c^2$

trigonometric ratios:

$\sin x = \dfrac{\text{opp}}{\text{hyp}}$ $\cos x = \dfrac{\text{adj}}{\text{hyp}}$ $\tan x = \dfrac{\text{opp}}{\text{adj}}$

Trigonometric formulae
sine rule $\dfrac{a}{\sin A} = \dfrac{b}{\sin B} = \dfrac{c}{\sin C}$

cosine rule $a^2 = b^2 + c^2 - 2bc \cos A$

area of triangle = $\dfrac{1}{2} ab \sin C$

Quadratic equations
The solutions of $ax^2 + bx + c = 0$, where $a \neq 0$,

Are given by $x = -b \pm \sqrt{\dfrac{b^2 - 4ac}{2a}}$

These formulae are listed by Edexcel as *need-to-know*. A poster highlighting them can be found on the Edexcel website.

REVISE MAPPING GUIDE

Pearson's *Revise* series provides simple, clear support to students preparing for their GCSE (9-1) exams. Parents or guardians may ask you if you know of any independent study resources that they can work through with their child, or you may wish to provide such resources yourself.

We have provided below a mapping guide for each lesson in this pack to a corresponding page in the *Revise* series, to make such recommendations easier for you.

For students studying Edexcel GCSE (9-1) Mathematics Higher, we recommend the following titles:
- *Revise* Edexcel GCSE (9–1) Mathematics Higher Revision Guide (ISBN: 9781447988090)
- *Revise* Edexcel GCSE (9–1) Mathematics Higher Revision Workbook (ISBN: 9781292210889)
- *Revise* Edexcel GCSE (9–1) Mathematics Higher Revision Cards (ISBN: 9781292173221)
- *Revise* Edexcel GCSE (9–1) Mathematics Higher Practice Papers Plus⁺ (ISBN: 9781292096315)

The Revision Guides and Revision Workbooks correspond page-for-page, so the page references are the same for both, and each Revision Card has the page reference in the top corner.

REVISE EDEXCEL GCSE (9–1) MATHEMATICS HIGHER REVISION GUIDE AND REVISION WORKBOOK

LESSON		WHAT'S IN THE BOOK?	PAGES
1	Diagnostic lesson	Find out what the student knows; Find out their preferences and attitudes	
	NUMBER		
2	Standard form	Standard form	8
3	Surds	Surds 1	12
4	Roots and indices	Indices 1; Indices 2; Surds 1	2, 3, 12
5	Factors and multiples	Factors and primes	1
6	Calculations	Calculator skills 1	4
7	Percentages and fractions	Fractions; Recurring decimals	5, 9
8	Rounding and estimation	Estimation	7
	ALGEBRA		
9	Introducing algebra	Algebraic expressions; Formulae; Rearranging formulae	16, 21, 46
10	Solving linear equations	Linear equations 1; Linear equations 2	19, 20
11	Solving quadratic equations	Factorising; Quadratic equations; The quadratic formula; Completing the square	18, 31, 32, 33
12	Simultaneous equations	Simultaneous equations 1; Simultaneous equations 2; Linear equations 1; Linear equations 2; Quadratic equations	34, 35, 19, 20, 31
13	Iteration	Iteration	45
14	Inequalities	Inequalities; Quadratic inequalities; Inequalities on graphs	37, 38, 41
15	Sequences	Arithmetic sequences; Solving sequence problems; Quadratic sequences	22, 23, 24
16	Linear, quadratic, cubic and reciprocal graphs	Straight-line graphs 1; Straight-line graphs 2; Parallel and perpendicular; Quadratic graphs; Cubic and reciprocal graphs; Sketching graphs	26, 26, 27, 28, 29, 44
17	Interpreting graphs	Real-life graphs; Turning points; Gradients of curves; Velocity–time graphs; Areas under curves	30, 43, 54, 55, 56
18	Trigonometric graphs and transformations	Trigonometric graphs; Transforming graphs; Functions; Inverse functions	39, 40, 50, 51
19	Graphs of circles	Equation of a circle	36

REVISE MAPPING GUIDE

REVISE EDEXCEL GCSE (9–1) MATHEMATICS HIGHER REVISION GUIDE AND REVISION WORKBOOK

MATHS
— HIGHER —

NEEDS ANALYSIS

FOR PARENTS AND GUARDIANS

We have a tutor because...
(Briefly explain why you have employed a tutor.)

Where we are currently...
(Briefly explain the student's current progress. Do you have access to reports and predicted grades?)

FOR STUDENTS

Use this space to tell your tutor about yourself.

I am...
Tell your tutor what type of person you think you are. Are you quiet or outgoing? Are you confident about your abilities?

I like...
Explain to your tutor how you like to work. Do you like to work independently or with more guidance? Do you like to write your answers down or talk through them first? Do you like to be creative?

How I feel about maths...
Do you like maths? Try to explain why or why not. What are your favourite and least favourite parts?

MATHS
— HIGHER —

Edexcel

NEEDS ANALYSIS

OUR GOALS

Work together to set small, achievable goals for the year ahead. Make them as positive as you can and don't limit your goals to areas of maths – think about personal development too. Together, look back at this list often to see how you are progressing.

TICK OFF EACH GOAL WHEN YOU'VE ACHIEVED IT

In four weeks' time, I will…

- ☐ ....
- ☐ ....
- ☐ ....
- ☐ ....
- ☐ ....
- ☐ ....

In three months' time, I will…

- ☐ ....
- ☐ ....
- ☐ ....
- ☐ ....
- ☐ ....
- ☐ ....

By the time I sit my exam, I will…

- ☐ ....
- ☐ ....
- ☐ ....
- ☐ ....
- ☐ ....
- ☐ ....

PROGRESS REPORT

Fill in the boxes below with help from your tutor.

My strengths are...
Which areas of maths do you think you've done well in recently? List at least three.

My favourite maths topic is...
Which maths topic is your favourite? It doesn't have to be the one you're best at!

because...

The areas of maths I need to work on are...
In which areas of maths do you think you need more practice?

To improve these areas, we are going to...
This space is for your tutor to explain how he/she is going to help you become confident in these areas.

END-OF-LESSON REPORT

We have looked at last week's homework and my tutor thinks...
This space is for your tutor to give feedback on last week's homework.

Today, we worked on...
This space is for you to list all of the topics and skills that you and your tutor have worked on today.

I feel...
This space is for you to explain how you feel about today's lesson. Did you enjoy it? Do you feel confident?

My tutor thinks...
This space is for your tutor to explain how the lesson went.

At home this week, we can...
This space is for your tutor to explain what your homework is and give you other ideas for extra revision and practice.

1 DIAGNOSTIC LESSON

LEARNING OBJECTIVES

- Know the properties of 2-D and 3-D shapes
- Multiply 3-digit by 2-digit whole numbers

SPECIFICATION LINKS

- G1, G2, G4, G6, A1, A4, A5, A22

STARTER ACTIVITY

- **Odd one out; 5 minutes; page 18**
  Ask the student to look at the three sets of shapes and decide which shape in each set is the 'odd one out'. The student must also explain their reasoning. Encourage the use of mathematical language and explain that there is more than one possible odd one out, depending on which features they consider, e.g. angles, sides.

MAIN ACTIVITIES

- **Algebraic manipulation; 20 minutes; page 19**
  Encourage the student to use appropriate mathematical language and to communicate their ideas to you. For question 1b, ask the student how they can make sure they find all possible solutions. Discuss systematic methods.
- **More than one method; 20 minutes; page 20**
  Before starting this activity, discuss with the student how each multiplication method works. Encourage the student to explain their reasoning. For example, for part b), ask: *How do you know what 127 × 4 is equal to?*

PLENARY ACTIVITY

- **Three things I have learned; 5 minutes**
  Ask the student to describe three things they have learned from this lesson. Encourage reflection on learning and let them know that it is okay to ask questions.

HOMEWORK ACTIVITY

- **Self-assessment; 15 minutes; page 21**
  Explain that the success of tutoring depends on the effort that both parties put into it. Ask the student to keep this in mind while completing the self-assessment table. Encourage the student to think carefully before answering each question. Explain that their answers are important because they will give you an idea of how best to support them.

SUPPORT IDEA

- **Algebraic manipulation** Before starting the activity, discuss with the student how to manipulate algebraic equations (by carrying out the same operation on both sides of the equation). You may wish to model this and show the student how a value can be added or subtracted from both sides, or how both sides can be multiplied or divided by the same value.

EXTENSION IDEA

- **More than one method** Challenge the student to write down as many related facts as they can using Ethan's method of long multiplication.

PROGRESS AND OBSERVATIONS

STARTER ACTIVITY: ODD ONE OUT

TIMING: 5 MINS

LEARNING OBJECTIVES

- Know the properties of 2-D and 3-D shapes

EQUIPMENT

1. Which shape is the odd one out in each set below? Circle your choice and give reasons for your answer.

a)

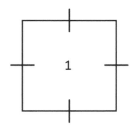 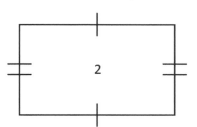 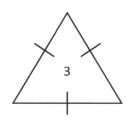

----

b)

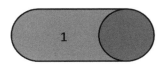 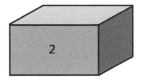

----

c)

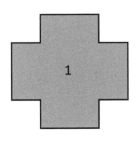 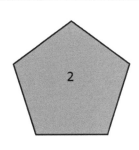 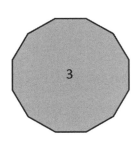

MAIN ACTIVITY: ALGEBRAIC MANIPULATION   TIMING: 20 MINS

LEARNING OBJECTIVES

- Manipulate algebraic expressions
- Substitute values into algebraic expressions
- Change the subject of an equation

EQUIPMENT

1. $2a + b = 20$

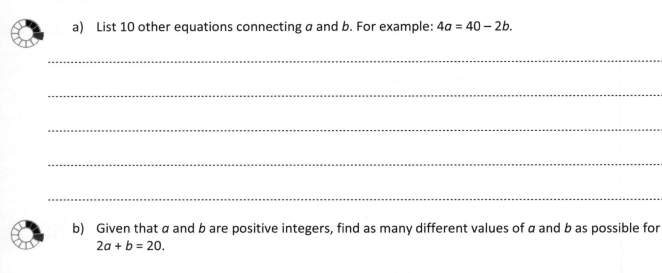

   a)   List 10 other equations connecting a and b. For example: $4a = 40 - 2b$.

   b)   Given that a and b are positive integers, find as many different values of a and b as possible for $2a + b = 20$.

   c)   Find the exact value of b when $a = \dfrac{13}{20}$.

   d)   Find the value of a in terms of b.

MAIN ACTIVITY: MORE THAN ONE METHOD

TIMING: 20 MINS

LEARNING OBJECTIVES

- Use formal methods of multiplication and division and understand place value

EQUIPMENT

- plain paper

Ethan and Amina have both worked out 24×127 using different methods.

Ethan

```
      1   2   7
  ×       2   4
 ─────────────────
      5   0   8
           1   2
  2   5   4   0
      1
 ─────────────────
  3   0   4   8
  1
```

Amina

×	100	20	7
20	2000	400	140
4	400	80	28

```
  2   0   0   0
      4   0   0
      1   4   0
      4   0   0
          8   0
  +       2   8
 ─────────────────
  3   0   4   8
  1       1
```

1. **Which method do you prefer? Explain why.**

----

2. **Use Ethan's working out to write down the answers to these calculations.**

   a) $127 \times 4 =$ _____

   b) $127 \times 20 =$ _____

   c) $3048 - 508 =$ _____

3. **Use Amina's working out to write down the answers to these calculations.**

   a) $20 \times 20 =$ _____

   b) $24 \times 7 =$ _____

   c) $3048 \div 24 =$ _____

4. **Use either method to write the answers to these calculations.**
   Explain to your tutor how you found each answer.

   a) $12.7 \times 24 =$ _____

   b) $0.24 \times 127 =$ _____

   c) $3048 \div 1270 =$ _____

   d) $0.127 \times 24 =$ _____

   e) $3048 \div 2.4 =$ _____

   f) $30.48 \div 127 =$ _____

HOMEWORK ACTIVITY: SELF-ASSESSMENT

TIMING: 15 MINS

LEARNING OBJECTIVES	EQUIPMENT
• Self-assessment of strengths and weaknesses	none

One way to develop your mathematical skills is to recognise your own weaknesses.

1. **Look at each of the statements below and decide how strongly you agree or disagree. Draw a tick in the box that applies to your answer. Make sure you answer truthfully!**

	Strongly agree	Somewhat agree	Somewhat disagree	Strongly disagree
I find all parts of maths difficult.				
I make silly mistakes in my calculations.				
I do not read the questions carefully.				
I get bored in maths and stop listening.				
I try as hard as I can in maths.				
I do not want to ask questions in case I look stupid.				
I understand maths during the lesson, but find it tricky when I have to do it on my own.				
I find problem solving difficult.				
I sometimes do not understand what maths questions are asking.				
I do not remember the methods I have been taught.				
There are some topics in maths that I have never understood.				
I do not understand why I need to learn some topics in maths.				

If you agreed or strongly agreed with either of the last two statements, list the topics that you were thinking of.

----

1 ANSWERS

STARTER ACTIVITY: ODD ONE OUT

1. The student's answers will vary, but here are some examples of reasoning.
a) Shape 2 is the odd one out because it has two marks on the short widths; shapes 1 and 3 have only one on each side.
or Shape 3 is the odd one out because it is a triangle (three-sided); shapes 1 and 2 are four-sided.
b) Shape 3 is the odd one out because it is shaded differently to shapes 1 and 2.
or Shape 2 is the odd one out because it is four-sided; shapes 1 and 3 are circular.
c) Shape 2 is the odd one out because it has only five sides, whereas shapes 1 and 3 have 12 sides each.

MAIN ACTIVITY: ALGEBRAIC MANIPULATION

1. a) Student's own answers. Examples of other equations connecting a and b in $2a + b = 20$ are:

$4a = 40 - 2b$	$6a = 60 - 4b$	$4a + 10 = 50 - 3b$
$8a = 80 - 6b$	$2a + 20 = 40 - 2b$	$3a - 10 = 20 + 3b$

b)
$a = 1, b = 18$	$a = 2, b = 16$	$a = 3, b = 14$
$a = 4, b = 12$	$a = 5, b = 10$	$a = 6, b = 8$
$a = 7, b = 6$	$a = 8, b = 4$	$a = 9, b = 2$

c) $18\dfrac{7}{10}$ d) $\dfrac{20-b}{2}$

MAIN ACTIVITY: MORE THAN ONE METHOD

1. Student's own answers. Examples may include:
Ethan's method is quicker and takes up less space.
Amina's method is easier because it is set out logically in the grid; there is less chance of making a mistake.

2. a) $127 \times 4 = 508$ b) $127 \times 20 = 2540$ c) $3048 - 508 = 2540$

3. a) $20 \times 20 = 400$ b) $24 \times 7 = 168$ c) $\dfrac{3048}{24} = 127$

4. a) $12.7 \times 24 = 304.8$ b) $0.24 \times 127 = 30.48$ c) $3048 \div 1270 = 2.4$
   d) $0.127 \times 24 = 3.048$ e) $3048 \div 2.4 = 1270$ f) $30.48 \div 127 = 0.24$

HOMEWORK ACTIVITY: SELF-ASSESSMENT

1. Student's own answers; if relevant, note the comments for the last two questions.

2 NUMBER: STANDARD FORM

LEARNING OBJECTIVES

- Calculate with and interpret standard form $A \times 10^n$ where $1 \leq A \leq 10$ and n is an integer

SPECIFICATION LINKS

- N9, N1, A4

STARTER ACTIVITY

- **Ordering numbers; 5 minutes; page 24**
  Ask the student to write the numbers shown in the cloud in ascending order.

MAIN ACTIVITIES

- **Writing numbers in standard form; 25 minutes; page 25**
  Show the student how to write very large and very small numbers in standard form and how to convert the numbers back to ordinary form. Then demonstrate how to input numbers in standard form on a calculator. Show the student how to carry out calculations involving standard form. Explain that multiplication and division questions in standard form can be simplified by combining the powers of 10, but for addition and subtraction questions, they should write the numbers as ordinary numbers first unless the power of 10 is the same.
- **Calculating with standard form; 15 minutes; page 26**
  Full instructions are given on the activity sheet.

PLENARY ACTIVITY

- **How to write in standard form; 5 minutes**
  Ask the student to explain, using fewer than 20 words, how to write a number in standard form.

HOMEWORK ACTIVITY

- **Exam-style questions; 45 minutes; page 27**
  Full instructions are given on the homework activity page.

SUPPORT IDEAS

- **Writing numbers in standard form** Support the student by writing the power of 10 in full, for example:
  $3.2 \times 10^5 = 3.2 \times 10 \times 10 \times 10 \times 10 \times 10$
- **Calculating with standard form** Support the student by modelling how to add, subtract, multiply and divide expressions written in standard form. When multiplying and dividing standard form numbers, group together the powers of 10 and write them in full, showing the student how to cancel. Remind the student to write their answers correctly in standard form with the numeric term between 0 and 10.

EXTENSION IDEA

- **Calculating with standard form** Ask the student to devise a rule for simplifying a multiplication or division when using numbers written in standard form. Link this to the laws of indices (that is, to multiply powers, add them; to divide powers, subtract them).

PROGRESS AND OBSERVATIONS

STARTER ACTIVITY: ORDERING NUMBERS

TIMING: 5 MINS

LEARNING OBJECTIVES

- Order positive numbers

EQUIPMENT

- calculator

1. **Write the numbers in this cloud in ascending order on the number line.**

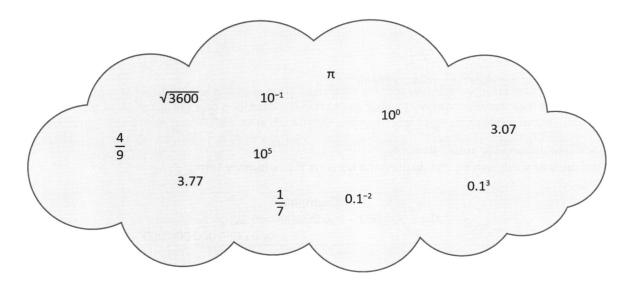

smallest   largest

MAIN ACTIVITY: WRITING NUMBERS IN STANDARD FORM   TIMING: 25 MINS

LEARNING OBJECTIVES	EQUIPMENT
• Write numbers in and interpret standard form	• calculator

1. Write each of these numbers in standard form.

a) 512 000 000   ....

b) 0.0000000356   ....

c) 272   ....

d) 0.1121   ....

2. Write each of these numbers in ordinary form.

a) 7.01×10^2 ....

b) 3.2×10^{-7} ....

3. Type each calculation into your calculator.
Write the answer as shown on the display and convert it to ordinary form.

> **Example:**
> $32\,000 \times 1\,900\,000 + 250\,000\,000 = 6.105 \times 10^{10}$
> $= 61\,050\,000\,000\,000$

a) $25\,000 \times 374\,000\,000 - 18\,000\,000$ ....

b) $\dfrac{4.5}{0.000000000015} - 24\,000\,000$ ....

c) 1×10^{-19} ....

d) $\sqrt{0.0000000144}$ ....

4. Sort these numbers from smallest to largest without writing them out as ordinary numbers.

4.5×10^{-2} 4.05×10^{-1} 4.005×10^4 4×10^8 4.05×10^{-5}

....

5. Find the answers to these questions. Give your answers in standard form.

a) $(2 \times 10^7) \times (3.5 \times 10^{11}) =$ ....

b) $\dfrac{3.2 \times 10^7}{2 \times 10^3} =$ ....

c) $(4.1 \times 10^7) + (1.5 \times 10^5) =$ ....

d) $(7.4 \times 10^6) - (3.7 \times 10^5) =$ ....

MAIN ACTIVITY: CALCULATING WITH STANDARD FORM   TIMING: 15 MINS

LEARNING OBJECTIVES	EQUIPMENT

- Calculate with standard form

- plain paper
- calculator

The table below shows the average distance from the Sun to the planets in our solar system.

Planet	Saturn	Venus	Jupiter	Neptune	Mars	Uranus	Mercury	Earth
Average distance from the Sun (km)	1.4×10^9	1.08×10^8	7.78×10^8	4.49×10^9	2.30×10^8	2.97×10^9	5.8×10^7	1.50×10^8

1. **Write the planets in order of distance from the Sun.**

closest ....

....   furthest

2. **Add together the distance from:**

a) the Sun to Mars and the Sun to Earth   ....

b) the Sun to Venus and the Sun to Mercury. ....

3. **Imagine that all the planets are in a straight line from the Sun. Work out the distance from:**

a) Uranus to Neptune   ....

b) Mercury to Saturn.   ....

4. **The speed of light is 1.08×10^9 km per hour. speed $= \dfrac{\text{distance}}{\text{time}}$**

a) How long does it take (in hours) for one of the Sun's rays to reach Earth? ....

b) Convert this time into minutes.   ....

5. **The diameter of a cell is 2.1×10^{-4} cm. A microscope enlarges the cell by different scale factors. Work out the diameter of the cell after it is enlarged by these scale factors.**

a) 100   ....

b) 50 000   ....

HOMEWORK ACTIVITY: EXAM-STYLE QUESTIONS

TIMING: 45 MINS

LEARNING OBJECTIVES

- Calculate with and interpret standard form $A \times 10^n$ where $1 \le A \le 10$ and n is an integer

EQUIPMENT

- calculator

6. Complete these questions without using a calculator.

a) Write 22 300 in standard form.

.... **(1 mark)**

b) Write 0.000506 in standard form.

.... **(1 mark)**

c) Work out the value of $(2.1 \times 10^3) + (3.5 \times 10^4)$. Write your answer in standard form.

.... **(2 marks)**

d) Work out the value of $(3.5 \times 10^2) \times (4 \times 10^3)$. Write your answer in standard form.

.... **(2 marks)**

e) Work out $(9 \times 10^{-5}) - (3.5 \times 10^{-5})$. Write your answer in standard form.

.... **(2 marks)**

f) Work out $(6.8 \times 10^7) \div (2 \times 10^3)$.

.... **(2 marks)**

7. You may use a calculator for these questions but you must show all your working.

a) The Earth has a diameter of 1.3×10^4 km. The distance between the Earth and the Sun is 1.5×10^8 km. How many times larger is the distance between the Earth and the Sun than the diameter of the Earth? Give your answer in standard form to 1 decimal place.

.... **(2 marks)**

b) The pages of a book are 9.1×10^{-2} mm thick. The front and back cover of the book are both 1 mm thick. How thick is a book with 350 pages? Give your answer to the nearest centimetre.

.... **(3 marks)**

8. One of the oldest fossils ever found is 3.45×10^9 years old. It is estimated that the Earth is 4.54 billion years old. How much older is the Earth than the fossil?

.... **(2 marks)**

2 ANSWERS

STARTER ACTIVITY: ORDERING NUMBERS

1. 0.1^3 (0.001), 10^{-1} (0.1), $\frac{1}{7}$ (0.143), $\frac{4}{9}$ (0.444), 10^0 (1), 3.07, π (3.14), 3.77, $\sqrt{3600}$ (60), 0.1^{-2} (100), 10^5 (100 000)

MAIN ACTIVITY: WRITING NUMBERS IN STANDARD FORM

1. a) 5.12×10^8 b) 3.56×10^{-8} c) 2.72×10^2 d) 1.121×10^{-1}
2. a) 701   b) 0.00000032
3. a) 9.349982×10^{12} = 9 349 982 000 000   b) 2.99976×10^{11} = 299 976 000 000
   c) 1×10^{-19} = 0.0000000000000000001   d) 1.2×10^{-4} = 0.00012
4. 4.05×10^{-5} (0.0000405), 4.5×10^{-2} (0.045), 4.05×10^{-1} (0.405), 4.005×10^4 (40050), 4×10^8 (400 000 000)
5. a) 7×10^{18} b) 1.6×10^4 c) 4.115×10^7 d) 7.03×10^6

MAIN ACTIVITY: CALCULATING WITH STANDARD FORM

1. Mercury, Venus, Earth, Mars, Jupiter, Saturn, Uranus, Neptune
2. a) 3.8×10^8 b) 1.66×10^8
3. a) 1.52×10^9 b) 1.342×10^9
4. a) $1.5 \times 10^8 \div 1.08 \times 10^9 = 0.14$ hours (2 dp)   b) $8\frac{1}{3}$ minutes
5. a) 0.021 cm   b) 10.5 cm

HOMEWORK ACTIVITY: EXAM-STYLE QUESTIONS

1. a) 2.23×10^4 b) 5.06×10^{-4} c) 3.71×10^4
   d) 1.4×10^6 e) 5.5×10^{-5} f) 3.4×10^4
2. a) 1.2×10^4 b) 3 cm
3. 1.09×10^9 years.

GLOSSARY

Standard form
A way of writing very large or small numbers in the form $A \times 10^n$ where $1 \leq A < 10$ and n is an integer

3 NUMBER: SURDS

LEARNING OBJECTIVES	SPECIFICATION LINKS
• Calculate exactly with surds	• N8

STARTER ACTIVITY

• **Square numbers; 5 minutes; page 30**
  Full instructions are given on the activity sheet.

MAIN ACTIVITIES

• **Simplifying expressions involving surds; 20 minutes; page 31**
  Explain that a surd is the root of a number. Show the student how a surd can be simplified by looking at the worked example. Establish that surds can be simplified by looking for square factors.

• **Rationalising the denominator; 20 minutes; page 32**
  Before starting the activity, explain to the student that if an expression of the form $(a + \sqrt{b})$ is multiplied by $(a - \sqrt{b})$, the solution will be rational.

PLENARY ACTIVITY

• **Teach me about surds; 5 minutes**
  Ask the student to imagine that you know nothing about surds. Give them five minutes to teach you as much as possible about surds.

HOMEWORK ACTIVITY

• **Solving problems involving surds; 40 minutes; page 33**
  Full instructions are given on the activity sheet.

SUPPORT IDEAS

• **Simplifying expressions involving surds** Before starting this activity, ask the student to list the square numbers to 100, and remind the student of the roots. Use this to support the activities.

• **Rationalising the denominator** Before the student attempts more complex fractions, model how to rationalise the denominator of a fraction when the denominator is in the form $\sqrt{a}$.

EXTENSION IDEA

• **Rationalising the denominator** Challenge the student to find as many different fractions as possible, with at least one irrational term in the denominator that will simplify to 3.

PROGRESS AND OBSERVATIONS

STARTER ACTIVITY: SQUARE NUMBERS

TIMING: 5 MINS

LEARNING OBJECTIVES

- Identify the pattern in the square numbers

EQUIPMENT

- pencil

1. **Shade all of the square numbers in this 100 grid. Describe any patterns you notice.**

1	2	3	4	5	6	7	8	9	10
11	12	13	14	15	16	17	18	19	20
21	22	23	24	25	26	27	28	29	30
31	32	33	34	35	36	37	38	39	40
41	42	43	44	45	46	47	48	49	50
51	52	53	54	55	56	57	58	59	60
61	62	63	64	65	66	67	68	69	70
71	72	73	74	75	76	77	78	79	80
81	82	83	84	85	86	87	88	89	90
91	92	93	94	95	96	97	98	99	100

MAIN ACTIVITY: SIMPLIFYING EXPRESSIONS INVOLVING SURDS   TIMING: 20 MINS

LEARNING OBJECTIVES

- Understand surd notation
- Simplify expressions involving surds

EQUIPMENT

Example:
Simplify $\sqrt{50}$.

$$\sqrt{50} = \sqrt{25 \times 2}$$
$$= \sqrt{25} \times \sqrt{2}$$
$$= 5\sqrt{2}$$

---

1. **Simplify these surds.**

   a) $\sqrt{200}$ ....

   b) $\sqrt{45}$ ....

   c) $\sqrt{80}$ ....

2. **Write your own question that is similar to question 1. Think carefully about how you know whether a surd can be simplified. Make sure you fill in the answers!**

   a) ....

   b) ....

   c) ....

3. **Simplify these expressions.**

   a) $\sqrt{12}$ ....

   b) $\sqrt{12} + \sqrt{75}$ ....

   c) $\sqrt{80} - \sqrt{45}$ ....

4. **List all of the possible pairs of surds below that will add to a single term. Explain how you know.**

   $\sqrt{8}$ $\sqrt{48}$ $\sqrt{50}$ $\sqrt{98}$ $\sqrt{175}$ $\sqrt{343}$

MAIN ACTIVITY: RATIONALISING THE DENOMINATOR   TIMING: **20** MINS

LEARNING OBJECTIVES
- Understand surd notation
- Simplify expressions involving surds

EQUIPMENT
none

Example:

Expand and simplify $(1+\sqrt{2})(3-\sqrt{2})$.

$$(1+\sqrt{2})(3-\sqrt{2}) = 1 \times 3 - 1 \times \sqrt{2} + 3 \times \sqrt{2} - \sqrt{2} \times \sqrt{2}$$
$$= 3 - \sqrt{2} + 3\sqrt{2} - 2$$
$$= 1 - 2\sqrt{2}$$

---

1. **This cloud contains eight expressions involving surds.**

   a) Choose four pairs of expressions from the cloud and find the product of the two expressions in each pair. Simplify your solutions as much as possible.

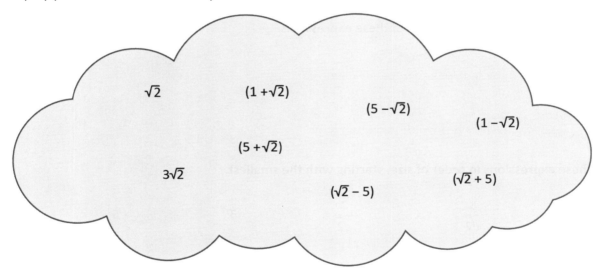

   b) Choose a pair of terms whose product is a rational number. Explain how you know.

----

2. **Rationalise the denominator in each of these fractions.**

   a) $\dfrac{3}{\sqrt{5}}$ ----------------------------

   b) $\dfrac{\sqrt{2}}{\sqrt{5}}$ ----------------------------

   c) $\dfrac{4}{(3+\sqrt{7})}$ ----------------------------

   d) $\dfrac{4+\sqrt{3}}{4-\sqrt{3}}$ ----------------------------

HOMEWORK ACTIVITY: SOLVING PROBLEMS INVOLVING SURDS   TIMING: 30 MINS

LEARNING OBJECTIVES	EQUIPMENT
• Understand surd notation • Simplify expressions involving surds	• none

1. **Write each of these expressions as a power of 2.**

    a) $\sqrt{2}$ ....

    b) $\dfrac{1}{\sqrt{2}}$ ....

    c) $\dfrac{1}{\sqrt[3]{2}}$ ....

    d) $\sqrt{16} \times 2^{-3}$ ....

    e) $\dfrac{4\sqrt{2}}{2^3}$ ....

2. **Rationalise the denominator of each of these expressions.**

    a) $\dfrac{3}{\sqrt{7}}$ ....

    b) $\dfrac{(2-\sqrt{5})}{(2+\sqrt{5})}$ ....

3. **Write these expressions in order of size, starting with the smallest.**

    $$\dfrac{1}{\sqrt{2}} \qquad\qquad \dfrac{2}{\sqrt{2}} \qquad\qquad 3^{-2} \qquad\qquad 5^0$$

    ....

4. **Show that** $\dfrac{3}{\sqrt{3}+\dfrac{1}{\sqrt{3}}} = \dfrac{3}{4}\sqrt{3}$.

    ....

    ....

3 Answers

Starter activity: Square numbers

1. 1, 4, 9, 16, 25, 36, 49, 64, 81 and 100 to be shaded. The difference between terms increases by two each time.

Main activity: Simplifying expressions involving surds

1. a) $10\sqrt{2}$ b) $3\sqrt{5}$ c) $4\sqrt{5}$
2. Check the student's answers.
3. a) $2\sqrt{3}$ b) $7\sqrt{3}$ c) $\sqrt{5}$
4. Pairs will simplify to give a single term if the surd part is equal.
Possible pairs are: $\sqrt{8}$ and $\sqrt{50}$, $\sqrt{8}$ and $\sqrt{98}$, $\sqrt{50}$ and $\sqrt{98}$, $\sqrt{48}$ and $\sqrt{144}$, $\sqrt{175}$ and $\sqrt{343}$

Main activity: Rationalising the denominator

1. a) Answers will vary depending on the pairs chosen.
b) $\sqrt{2}$ and $3\sqrt{2}$, $(1+\sqrt{2})$ and $(1-\sqrt{2})$, $(5-\sqrt{2})$ and $(5+\sqrt{2})$, $(\sqrt{2}-5)$ and $(\sqrt{2}+5)$

2. a) $\dfrac{3\sqrt{5}}{5}$ b) $\dfrac{\sqrt{10}}{5}$ c) $6-2\sqrt{7}$ d) $\dfrac{19+8\sqrt{3}}{13}$

Homework activity: Solving problems involving surds

1. a) $2^{\frac{1}{2}}$ b) $2^{-\frac{1}{2}}$ c) $2^{-\frac{1}{3}}$ d) 2^{-1} e) $2^{-\frac{1}{2}}$

2. a) $\dfrac{3\sqrt{7}}{7}$ b) $-9-4\sqrt{5}$

3. 3^{-2} $\dfrac{1}{\sqrt{2}}$ 5^{0} $\dfrac{2}{\sqrt{2}}$

4.
$$\frac{3}{\sqrt{3}+\dfrac{1}{\sqrt{3}}} \times \left(\frac{\sqrt{3}}{\sqrt{3}}\right) = \frac{3\sqrt{3}}{\sqrt{3}+\dfrac{\sqrt{3}}{\sqrt{3}}}$$
$$= \frac{3\sqrt{3}}{3+1}$$
$$= \frac{3\sqrt{3}}{4}$$
$$= \frac{3}{4}\sqrt{3}$$

Glossary

Surd
An irrational number, expressed as the root of an integer

4 NUMBER: ROOTS AND INDICES

LEARNING OBJECTIVES

- Use positive integer powers and roots
- Calculate with roots and integer and fractional indices

SPECIFICATION LINKS

- N3, N6, N7, N8, A4

STARTER ACTIVITY

- **Heads and tails; 5 minutes; page 36**
  Ask the student to match each 'head' in the table to its correct 'tail'.

MAIN ACTIVITIES

- **Reciprocals and laws of indices; 20 minutes; page 37**
  Revise the idea of a reciprocal and what it means, modelling finding the reciprocal of decimals and of whole numbers. Discuss how a number can be raised to a negative power and model some examples. Remind the student of the meaning of index notation, focusing on the laws $a^1 = a$ and $a^0 = 1$. Be sure to clear up the common misconception that $a^0 = 0$.
- **Fractional indices; 20 minutes; page 38**
  Revise the meaning of fractional indices and link this to surds.

PLENARY ACTIVITY

- **Blind challenge; 5 minutes**
  Cover all activity sheets and ask the student to list all the facts they know about indices, including decimal and negative indices.

HOMEWORK ACTIVITY

- **Indices practice; 40 minutes; page 39**
  Full instructions are given on the activity sheet.

SUPPORT IDEA

- **Reciprocals and laws of indices** Support the student's understanding of this by expanding the expressions, for example:
  $3^4 \times 3^8 = 3 \times 3 \times 3 \times 3 \times 3 \times 3 \times 3 \times 3 \times 3 \times 3 \times 3 \times 3$

EXTENSION IDEA

- **Reciprocals and laws of indices** Link this task to standard form and discuss how to find the product and quotient of the number written in standard form.

PROGRESS AND OBSERVATIONS

STARTER ACTIVITY: HEADS AND TAILS

TIMING: 5 MINS

LEARNING OBJECTIVES

• Recognise powers and roots of whole numbers

EQUIPMENT

1. Justine is making coins. The values on the head and tail sides of each coin must be equal.
   Draw lines to match up the heads (dark grey) and tails (light grey) to show the pairs of values she should write on each coin. Do not use a calculator.

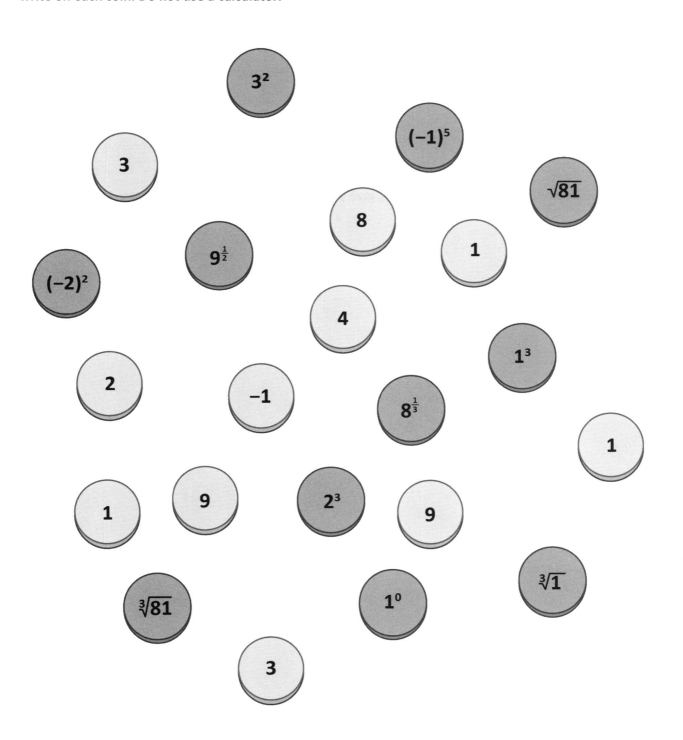

MATHS
— HIGHER —

Edexcel

MAIN ACTIVITY: RECIPROCALS AND LAWS OF INDICES   **TIMING: 20 MINS**

LEARNING OBJECTIVES

- Use positive and negative integer powers
- Calculate with integer indices
- Know and use the term reciprocal

EQUIPMENT

- calculator

The reciprocal of a number is found by dividing 1 by that number. The reciprocal of 3 is $\frac{1}{3}$.

You can also write the reciprocal by writing the number to the power of −1, so the reciprocal of 3 is 3^{-1}.

 1. Find the reciprocal of each of these numbers.

   a) 7   ....

   c) 0.25   ....

   b) $\frac{1}{3}$ ....

   d) $\frac{3}{4}$ ....

 2. Work out the value of these numbers. You may give your answers as fractions or decimals.

   a) 8^{-1} ....

   b) 0.1^{-1} ....

   c) 20^{-1} ....

 3. Complete these laws of indices.

   a) $a^x \times a^y =$ ....

   c) $\dfrac{a^x}{a^y} =$ ....

   e) $(a^x)^y =$ ....

   b) $a^{-x} =$ ....

   d) $a^0 =$ ....

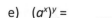 **4. Work out the exact value of each of these expressions.**

   a) 3^{-3} ....

   b) $3^{-4} \times 3^8$ ....

   c) $\dfrac{5^{-3}}{5^{-4}}$ ....

   d) $\dfrac{9^{-2} \times 9^{-2}}{9^{-3} \times 9^{-1}}$ ....

MAIN ACTIVITY: FRACTIONAL INDICES

TIMING: 20 MINS

LEARNING OBJECTIVES

- Calculate with fractional indices

EQUIPMENT

- calculator

The square root of 5 can be written as a surd: $\sqrt{5}$ or as a fractional power: $5^{\frac{1}{2}}$

The cube root of 5 can be written as a surd: $\sqrt[3]{5}$ or as a fractional power: $5^{\frac{1}{3}}$

Fractional power can be written as: $a^{\frac{1}{x}} = \sqrt[x]{a}$ or as: $a^{\frac{x}{y}} = \sqrt[y]{a^x}$

1. **Work out the value of each of these numbers.**

   a) $4^{\frac{1}{2}}$ ....

   b) $27^{\frac{1}{3}}$ ....

   c) $1^{\frac{1}{5}}$ ....

2. **Write each of these expressions as a power of x.**

   a) $\sqrt{x}$ ....

   b) $\sqrt[3]{x^4}$ ....

   c) $\sqrt[4]{x}$ ....

   d) $\sqrt[5]{x^3}$ ....

3. **Find the value of each of these numbers.**

   a) $100^{\frac{3}{2}}$ ....

   b) $8^{\frac{2}{3}}$ ....

   c) $1^{\frac{3}{2}}$ ....

   d) $\left(\dfrac{8}{27}\right)^{-\frac{2}{3}}$ ....

4. **Write each of these numbers as a power of 2.**

   a) $8^{\frac{1}{2}}$ ....

   b) $\sqrt[5]{4^3}$ ....

   c) $\dfrac{2^{\frac{1}{2}}}{2^{\frac{3}{4}}}$ ....

HOMEWORK ACTIVITY: INDICES PRACTICE

TIMING: 40 MINS

LEARNING OBJECTIVES
- Use positive integer powers and roots
- Calculate with roots and integer indices
- Calculate with fractions

EQUIPMENT
none

1. **What is the value of $16^{\frac{1}{2}}$? Circle your answer and give a reason why.**

    8   64 $\frac{1}{256}$ 4 $\frac{1}{4}$

    ....

    ....

2. **Write these numbers in order of size, starting with the smallest.**

    $2^4 \times 2^2$ $\frac{2^{11}}{2^7}$ $\left(2^3\right)^3$

    ....

 3. **Find the value of x in this identity:**  $1000^{-\frac{x}{3}} = 0.01$ ....

4. **Which is larger: 3^4 or 4^3?** ....

 5. **What is $\dfrac{5^7 \times 5^{-3}}{5^{-\frac{3}{2}}}$ written as a single power of 5? Circle your answer and show your working.**

    $5^{-\frac{41}{3}}$ $5^{\frac{23}{2}}$ $5^{\frac{11}{2}}$ $5^{\frac{14}{3}}$ $5^{\frac{11}{2}}$

    ....

6. **What are the values a and b in this identity: $4^{\frac{a}{b}} = \left(\dfrac{1}{64}\right)^{\frac{1}{2}}$?**

    $a =$ .... $b =$ ....

7. **What is the reciprocal of $8^{\frac{1}{3}}$?** ....

8. **Write $\sqrt[3]{32}$ as a power of 2.** ....

39

4 Answers

Starter activity: Heads and tails

1. $3^2 = 9$ $9^{\frac{1}{2}} = 3$ $1^3 = 1$ $\sqrt{81} = 9$ $2^3 = 8$ $8^{\frac{1}{3}} = 2$

$(-2)^2 = 4$ $(-1)^5 = -1$ $\sqrt[3]{81} = 3$ $\sqrt[3]{1} = 1$ $1^0 = 1$

Main activity: Reciprocals and laws of indices

1. a) $\dfrac{1}{7}$ b) 3   c) 4   d) $\dfrac{4}{3}$

2. a) $\dfrac{1}{8}$ b) 10   c) $\dfrac{1}{20}$

3. a^{x+y} b) $\dfrac{1}{a^x}$ c) a^{x-y} d) 1   e) $a^{x \times y}$

4. a) $\dfrac{1}{27}$ b) 81   c) 5   d) 1

Main activity: Fractional indices

1. a) 2   b) 3   c) 1

2. a) $x^{\frac{1}{2}}$ b) $x^{\frac{4}{3}}$ c) $x^{\frac{1}{4}}$ d) $x^{\frac{3}{5}}$

3. a) 1000   b) 4   c) 1   d) $\dfrac{9}{4} = 2.25$

4. a) $2^{\frac{3}{2}}$ b) $2^{\frac{6}{5}}$ c) $2^{-\frac{1}{4}}$

Homework activity: Indices practice

1. 4 because $16^{\frac{1}{2}} = \sqrt{16}$

2. $\dfrac{2^{11}}{2^7}$ $2^4 \times 2^2$ $\left(2^3\right)^3$

3. 2

4. 3^4

5. $5^{\frac{11}{2}}$

6. $a = -3$ $b = 2$

7. $\dfrac{1}{2}$

8. $2^{\frac{5}{3}}$

Glossary

Index/Indices/Power/Exponent
A number that indicates how many times to multiply the base number by itself

5 NUMBER: FACTORS AND MULTIPLES

LEARNING OBJECTIVES

- Use the concept and vocabulary of prime factorisation and the unique factorisation theorem
- Find the highest common factor and lowest common multiple of a set of numbers using prime factorisation methods

SPECIFICATION LINKS

- N4

STARTER ACTIVITY

- **Numbers 1 to 20; 5 minutes; page 42**
  Full instructions are given on the activity sheet.

MAIN ACTIVITIES

- **Unique factorisation theorem; 15 minutes; page 43**
  Remind the student how to draw factor trees. Question 2 encourages the student to recognise that the prime factor decomposition of a positive integer is unique.
- **Finding the HCF and LCM; 25 minutes; page 44**
  Work through the worked example with the student, showing how to construct the Venn diagram. Then ask the student to complete the questions by following the instructions on the page.

PLENARY ACTIVITY

- **True/false; 5 minutes**
  Ask the student to decide if the following statements are true or false and to explain their answers.
  a) If the prime factor decomposition of an integer includes a 2 then the number is even (false).
  b) The product of two primes is always odd (false).
  c) Two integers will always have at least one common factor (true).

HOMEWORK ACTIVITY

- **HCF and LCM problems; 30 minutes; page 45**
  Full instructions are given on the activity sheet.

SUPPORT IDEA

- **Unique factorisation theorem** Spend some time practising the skill of prime factor decomposition using factor trees before attempting question 2.

EXTENSION IDEA

- **Finding the HCF and LCM** Ask the student to design their own problem-solving style question that involves finding the HCF or the LCM.

PROGRESS AND OBSERVATIONS

STARTER ACTIVITY: NUMBERS 1 TO 20

TIMING: 5 MINS

LEARNING OBJECTIVES

- Use the concepts and vocabulary of prime numbers, factors, multiples, squares, cubes

EQUIPMENT

1. **List the integers between 1 and 20 that are none of the following:**

   - prime

   - a factor of 12

   - a multiple of 4

   - square

   - cube

MAIN ACTIVITY: UNIQUE FACTORISATION THEOREM   **TIMING: 15 MINS**

LEARNING OBJECTIVES

• Use the concept and vocabulary of prime factorisation and the unique factorisation theorem

EQUIPMENT

1. List the factors of each of these numbers.

a)   12   ....

b)   100   ....

c)   180   ....

2. Use factor trees to write 120 as a product of prime factors.

a)   Complete this factor tree of 120 and use this to write 120 as a product of prime factors using indices.

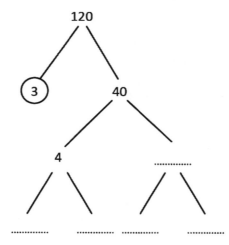

--   --

b)   Next to the factor tree above, draw a different factor tree for 120 and use this to write 120 as a product of prime factors.

c)   What do you notice? Why is this?

----

3. Write these numbers as a product of prime factors using indices.

a)   280   ....   b)   825   ....

4. The factors of a number include 1, 2, 3, 4, 5 and 6. What is the smallest number it could be? Give a reason for your answer.

MATHS
— HIGHER —

Edexcel

MAIN ACTIVITY: FINDING THE HCF AND LCM　　　　　**TIMING: 25 MINS**

LEARNING OBJECTIVES

- Use the concept and vocabulary of prime factorisation and the unique factorisation theorem
- Find the highest common factor and lowest common multiple of a set of numbers using prime factorisation methods

EQUIPMENT

- plain paper

1. **List the factors of 60 and 45. What is the highest common factor (HCF)?**

---

2. **List the first few multiples of 60 and 45. What is their lowest common multiple (LCM)?**

Example:
Find the HCF and LCM of 45 and 60 using a Venn diagram.

$45 = 3 \times 3 \times 5$
$60 = 2 \times 2 \times 3 \times 5$
$HCF = 3 \times 5$
$= 15$
$LCM = 2 \times 2 \times 3 \times 3 \times 5$
$= 180$

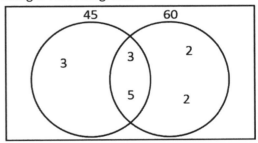

3. **Use the Venn diagram method to find the HCF and LCM of each of these groups of numbers. Show your diagrams on a separate piece of paper.**

　a)　210 and 60　　　　　　　　　　b)　385, 165 and 30

4. **Which method do you prefer? Explain why.**

---

5. **The HCF of a pair of numbers is 20. The LCM is 300. What are the numbers?**

HOMEWORK ACTIVITY: HCF AND LCM PROBLEMS

TIMING: 30 MINS

LEARNING OBJECTIVES	EQUIPMENT
• Use the concept and vocabulary of prime factorisation and the unique factorisation theorem • Find the highest common factor and lowest common multiple of a set of numbers using prime factorisation methods	none

1. Given that $90 = 2 \times 3^2 \times 5$, write each of the following numbers as a product of prime factors using indices.

   a) 180 ....

   b) 9000 ....

2. $4410 = 2 \times 3^2 \times 5 \times 7^2$ and $147 = 3 \times 7^2$. What is the value of $4410 \div 147$? Show your working.

   ....

   ....

   ....

3. Coloured beads come in bags of different sizes.
   Green beads come in bags of 12.
   Red beads come in bags of 15.
   Blue beads come in bags of 20.
   Alice buys the same number of beads of each colour.
   What is the smallest number of beads she could have bought? Show your working.

   ....

   ....

   ....

4. The students at a school can be split into 15 equal-sized classes or 21 equal-sized classes.
   What is the smallest number of students that attend the school?

   ....

   ....

5 ANSWERS

STARTER ACTIVITY: NUMBERS 1 TO 20

1. 10, 14, 15 and 18

MAIN ACTIVITY: UNIQUE FACTORISATION THEOREM

1. a) 1, 2, 3, 4, 6, 12   b) 1, 2, 4, 5, 10, 20, 25, 50, 100
c) 1, 2, 3, 4, 5, 6, 9, 10, 12, 15, 18, 20, 30, 36, 45, 60, 90, 180

2. a)   120 as a product of prime factors using indices is $2^3 \times 3 \times 5$.

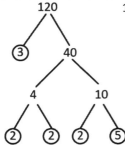

b) Example of a different factor tree that the student might suggest: see diagram above right. Here, 120 as a product of prime factors using indices is $2^3 \times 3 \times 5$.
c) The numbers are the same as in part a). The solution is unique.

3. a) $2^3 \times 5 \times 7$ b) $3 \times 5^2 \times 11$

4. 60. Explanation: 1×60, 2×30, 3×20, 4×15, 5×12, 6×10

MAIN ACTIVITY: FINDING THE HCF AND LCM

1. Factors of 60: 1, 2, 3, 4, 5, 6, 10, 12, 15, 20, 30, 60
Factors of 45: 1, 3, 5, 9, 15, 45
HCF = 15

2. Multiples of 60: 60, 120, 180, 240, ...
Multiples of 45: 45, 90, 135, 180, 225, ...
LCM = 180

3. a) HCF = 30, LCM = 420
b) HCF = 5, LCM = 2310

4. Student's own answer

5. 60 and 100

HOMEWORK ACTIVITY: HCF AND LCM PROBLEMS

1. a) $2^2 \times 3^2 \times 5$ b) $2^3 \times 3^2 \times 5^3$

2. 30

3. 120 beads

4. 105

GLOSSARY

Highest common factor (HCF)
The largest integer that will divide exactly into two or more numbers

Lowest common multiple (LCM)
The smallest integer that will divide exactly by two or more numbers

6 Number: Calculations

Learning objectives

- Calculate with fractions
- Calculate with multiples of π
- Estimate powers and roots of any given number

Specification links

- N1, N2, N3, N4, N6, N7, N8

Starter activity

- **Order, order; 5 minutes; page 48**
  Ask the student to order the fractions and decimals. Encourage him or her to discuss their reasoning and to try to think of the most simple approach to this.

Main activities

- **Exact calculations; 25 minutes; page 49**
  Explain that sometimes, we need to leave solutions in exact terms, which can include the use of fractions and π.
  Tell the student that π can be treated in the same way as an algebraic term – it is just a symbol representing a number. Remind the student how to convert between a mixed number and an improper fraction. Establish how to carry out the four operations with fractions (include using cross-cancelling to simplify calculations for multiplication and division).
- **Estimating powers and roots; 15 minutes; page 50**
  Before the student begins this activity, remind them that when finding the root of a value, there are always two solutions, one positive and one negative, unless the value is 0.

Plenary activity

- **The four operations with fractions; 5 minutes**
  Ask the student to draw flow charts to show how to add, subtract, multiply or divide fractions.

Homework activity

- **Poster; 40 minutes; page 51**
  Full instructions are given on the activity sheet.

Support ideas

- **Exact calculations** Start with fractions that are not mixed numbers and work through some examples before asking the student to try the activity sheet.
- **Estimating powers and roots** Support the student by writing out the first 12 square numbers.

Extension idea

- **Estimating powers and roots** Sketch the graph of $y = x^2$ on graph paper. Use this to find the exact roots in question 2 on the activity sheet.

Progress and observations

STARTER ACTIVITY: ORDER, ORDER

TIMING: 5 MINS

LEARNING OBJECTIVES

* Order positive and negative decimals and ratios

EQUIPMENT

1. **Write these numbers in order of size, starting with the smallest. Explain your method below.**

$$-\frac{7}{8} \qquad \frac{2}{3} \qquad -\frac{18}{19} \qquad -0.45 \qquad -\frac{21}{20} \qquad -\frac{23}{25}$$

....

MATHS
— HIGHER —

Edexcel

TUTORS' GUILD

MAIN ACTIVITY: EXACT CALCULATIONS

TIMING: 25 MINS

LEARNING OBJECTIVES

- Calculate exactly with fractions and multiples of π

EQUIPMENT

- three dice

Answer these questions without using a calculator.

Mixed number calculations

For this game, generate mixed numbers by rolling three dice.

For example, if the dice land on 2, 3 and 5, you could make the mixed numbers $3\frac{2}{5}$ or $5\frac{2}{3}$.

Your numerator must not be larger than your denominator.

1. **Roll the three dice twice to create two mixed numbers.**

   a) Add the numbers. ....

   b) Subtract the smaller number from the larger number. ....

   c) Multiply the numbers together. ....

   d) Divide the larger number by the smaller number. ....

   e) What is the largest possible answer to part a)? Assume all six numbers rolled are different.

....

Working with π

2. **Roll two dice to give the missing values in the following calculations. Find an exact solution for each.**

   a) $\dfrac{\pi}{.....} + \dfrac{\pi}{.....} =$ ....

   b) $\dfrac{5\pi}{.....} - \dfrac{.....\pi}{2} =$ ....

   c) $\dfrac{.....\pi}{.....} \times \dfrac{\pi}{4} =$ ....

   d) $\dfrac{\pi}{.....} \div \dfrac{\pi}{.....} =$ ....

MATHS
— HIGHER —

Edexcel

MAIN ACTIVITY: ESTIMATING POWERS AND ROOTS TIMING: 15 MINS

LEARNING OBJECTIVES
- Estimate powers and roots of any given number

EQUIPMENT
- random number generator or 1–9 dice
- calculator

1. Use a random number generator or roll a 1–9 dice and roll it three times to generate three numbers. Use these values in order to give you a decimal number between 1 and 10. Find an estimate of the square of the value.

2. Roll the dice twice to create a decimal number between 1 and 0. For example, if you roll 2 and 5, you would get the decimal number 0.25. Find the exact square of this value.

> **Example:**
> Estimate the value of $\sqrt{107}$.
>
> $10^2 = 100$ and $11^2 = 121$, so $10 < \sqrt{107} < 11$
> Because 107 lies nearer to 100 than to 121, a good estimate for $\sqrt{107}$ would be $\approx \pm 10.3$.

3. Estimate the square root of each of these values. Check your answers on a calculator.

   a) 75

   b) 12

   c) 98

   d) 150

4. Use prime factor decomposition to write 44 100 as a product of primes using indices. Explain how you could now easily find $\sqrt{44100}$.

HOMEWORK ACTIVITY: POSTER

TIMING: 40 MINS

LEARNING OBJECTIVES	EQUIPMENT
• Calculate with roots and integer indices	none
• Calculate with fractions	

 1. Design a poster to show how to carry out each of the following mathematical operations.

- How to add fractions

- How to subtract fractions

- How to multiply fractions

- How to divide fractions

- How to estimate the root of a number

Try to make it bright and clear so you can use it for revision closer to the exam.

Try to include the following words:

- simplify

- common denominator

- improper fraction

- mixed number

- square

6 ANSWERS

STARTER ACTIVITY: ORDER, ORDER

1. $-\dfrac{21}{20}$ $-\dfrac{18}{19}$ $-\dfrac{23}{25}$ $-\dfrac{7}{8}$ -0.45 $\dfrac{2}{3}$

MAIN ACTIVITY: EXACT CALCULATIONS

1. a)–d) Student's own answers

e) The largest solution could be found by adding $6\dfrac{3}{4}$ and $5\dfrac{1}{2}$.

2. a)–d) Check the student's solutions.

MAIN ACTIVITY: ESTIMATING POWERS AND ROOTS

1. Check the student's answers.
2. Check the student's answers.
3. a) ±8.7   b) ±3.5   c) ±9.9   d) ±12.2
4. 44 100 = $2^2 \times 3^2 \times 5^2 \times 7^2$ You can root each value, giving: 2 × 3 × 5 × 7 = ±210

HOMEWORK ACTIVITY: POSTER

1. Check the student's poster.

GLOSSARY

Root

The root of x is a number which, when multiplied by itself, gives x.

7 NUMBER: PERCENTAGES AND FRACTIONS

LEARNING OBJECTIVES

- Convert percentages to fractions and decimals
- Find the percentage of a number including using a multiplier, and solve problems involving percentage change, including simple and compound interest, and growth and decay, and original value problems
- Express one quantity as a percentage of another and calculate percentage change

SPECIFICATION LINKS

N10, N11, N12, N13

STARTER ACTIVITY

- **What is missing?; 5 minutes; page 54**
  Remind the student that any percentage can be written as a fraction or a decimal. Model this if necessary. Ask the student to identify which term is missing. Each percentage should have an equivalent fraction and decimal.

MAIN ACTIVITIES

- **Calculating with percentages and fractions; 25 minutes; page 55**
  Establish how to find percentages and fractions of numbers, both mentally (using familiar percentages such as 50%, 10% and 1%) and using a multiplier. Discuss how to calculate percentage change using a multiplier and how to find the original price, given the new price and percentage change. Discuss how to solve compound interest and original price problems. Work through the problems on the page, choosing the appropriate level for the student.

- **Repeated change; 15 minutes; page 56**
  Establish the difference between simple and compound interest. Work through the task with the student, encouraging them to recognise that a simple way of calculating the compound interest is to multiply by 1.03^5. Explain that 'depreciation' is the inverse of 'appreciation'. Discuss how these problems might be solved using a multiplier raised to a power.

PLENARY ACTIVITY

- **Describe the method; 5 minutes**
  Ask the student to explain to you how they would find: a) 20% without a calculator   b) 17% with a calculator
  c) the new price of an item if the price increases by 12%   d) the difference between compound and simple interest
  e) the percentage change if the original price was £12 and the new price is £15.

HOMEWORK ACTIVITY

- **How hot?; 60 minutes; page 57**
  Tailor the homework to support the work completed during the lesson. The student should complete some or all of the questions in the grid, depending on how well they have performed and how much practice they need.

SUPPORT IDEA

- **Calculating with percentages and fractions** The student may find it easier to calculate percentages if they first divide by 100 to find 1% and then multiply up to find the percentage required. Model this and encourage the student to use this method to calculate percentages until they are comfortable finding other methods, such as dividing by 5 to find 20%.

EXTENSION IDEA

- **Repeated change** Develop question 1 by asking the student how they could work out the minimum amount of time it would take for the amount in the account to be over £600.

PROGRESS AND OBSERVATIONS

STARTER ACTIVITY: WHAT IS MISSING?

TIMING: 5 MINS

LEARNING OBJECTIVES
- Convert between fractions, decimals and percentages

EQUIPMENT
none

1. **Each percentage in the cloud should have an equivalent decimal and fraction. Find the missing value.**

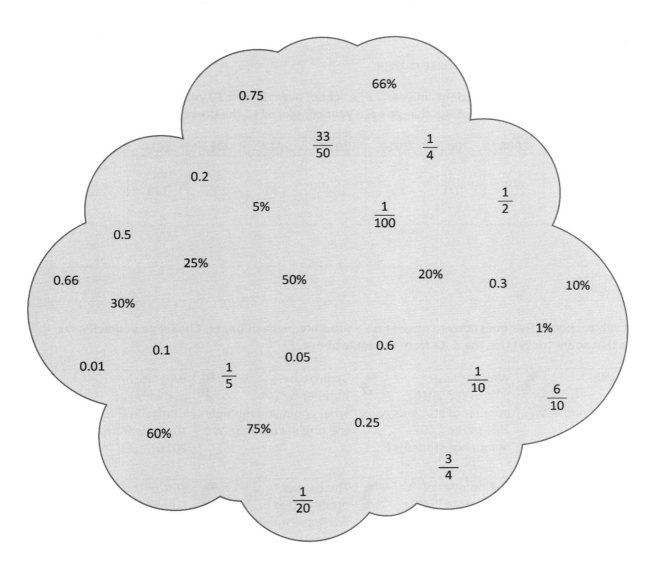

MAIN ACTIVITY: CALCULATING WITH PERCENTAGES AND FRACTIONS   TIMING: 25 MINS

LEARNING OBJECTIVES

- Find percentages and fractions of a number with and without a calculator
- Use percentages to solve problems
- Interpret fractions and percentages as operators
- Express one quantity as a percentage of another and calculate percentage change
- Calculate original value after a percentage change

EQUIPMENT

- scientific calculator
- plain paper

 1. **This table shows the number of students in year 7 of a school over the last 10 years. Explain how to work out the percentage change each year compared to the previous year.**

Year	2007	2008	2009	2010	2011	2012	2013	2014	2015	2016
Number of students in year seven	95	107	100	117	134	136	135	128	112	110

2. **From this table, choose five questions to answer on a separate piece of paper. Challenge yourself – try questions that seem tricky! Use the data from the table above.**

What decimal would you multiply by to find 80%?	Which is larger – 50% of the 2010 number of students or 75% of the 2007 number of students?	To increase a number by 20%, what could you multiply the original number by?	What is the percentage change in the number of students from 2015 to 2016?
What is the percentage increase in the number of students from 2007 to 2016?	The number of students in 2006 was 80% of the number in 2007. How many students were there in 2006?	The council predicts that in 2020, the number of students will be 140% of the number in 2016. How many students will there be if they are correct?	75% of the number of students in 2004 is 60. How many students were there in 2004?
Work out the percentage increase in the number of students from 2010 to 2011, and from 2011 to 2012. When was the greatest percentage increase?	What percentage of the number of students in 2011 were there in 2007?	In 2017, there will be 20% more students than there were in 2016. How many students will there be?	At another school, there were 117 students in 2016. This was 10% fewer than in 2015. How many students were there in 2015?

MAIN ACTIVITY: REPEATED CHANGE

TIMING: 15 MINS

LEARNING OBJECTIVES

- Calculate using simple and compound interest
- Find an increase or decrease using a multiplier raised to a power

EQUIPMENT

- scientific calculator

1. **Two bank accounts offer different savings rates:**

Account A:	Account B:
3% compound interest	5% simple interest

   Eric wishes to invest £500 in the bank for 5 years.

   Work out which account Eric should use. Show your working.

   ----

2. **The values of two cars depreciate at different rates per year.**

   Car A: purchase price £32 500   depreciation 20% per annum

   Car B: purchase price £27 000   depreciation 15% per annum

   Which car will be worth more after 4 years? Show your working.

   ----

3. **The cost of Car C was originally £45 000. Given that the value depreciates at a rate of 10% per annum, and that the car is now worth £32 805, how old is the car?**

HOMEWORK ACTIVITY: HOW HOT?

TIMING: 60 MINS

LEARNING OBJECTIVES

- Convert percentages to fractions and decimals
- Find the percentage of a number including using a multiplier, and solve problems involving percentage change, including simple and compound interest, and growth and decay, and original value problems
- Express one quantity as a percentage of another and calculate percentage change

EQUIPMENT

- scientific calculator

1. **There are 19 challenges in the table below. Each row has a different difficulty – the more chillies, the 'hotter' the challenge. Your tutor will tell you how many questions to complete, but you should collect at least 10 chillies. Answer at least one question from each row.**

Find 65% of 30 inches without using a calculator.	Find 73% of £380. You may use a calculator but show your working.	Reduce 500 by 17%. You may use a calculator but show your working.	Which is larger, 20% of £50 or 25% of £60?
The price of a pair of shoes has increased from £40 to £45. What is the percentage change?	Mr Barros invested £2000 in a bank with simple interest of 3% per annum. How much will he have in the account after two years?	In one year, a child grew from 103 cm to 109 cm. Work out the percentage change in height. Give your answer to 1 significant figure.	The surface area of an ice cap decreases by 10% each year. If the area is 1750 m² this year, what will it be in four years?
I think of a number. 30% of that number is 15. What number am I thinking of?	In a sale, all prices are reduced by 30%. If the sale price of a washing machine is £245, what was the original price?	If 13% of a number is 7.8, what was the original number?	Prices in a shop are all increased by 5%. A shirt now costs £63. What was the original price?
A bank account gives 3% compound interest on savings. Eric invests £1500. How long will he have to invest it for before he has over £1700 in the account?	The value of a bike depreciates by 20% each year. After two years, the value is £76.80. How much did the bike originally cost?	A painting increases in value by 35% each year. In 2017, it is worth £1640.25. How much was it worth in 2015?	A car depreciates in value at the rate of 20% per annum. If it is worth £16 000 in 2017, how much was it worth in 2014?

7 ANSWERS

STARTER ACTIVITY: WHAT IS MISSING?

1. $\dfrac{3}{10}$

MAIN ACTIVITY: CALCULATING WITH PERCENTAGES AND FRACTIONS

1. Subtract the new amount from the original amount, divide by the original amount and multiply by 100.
2.

0.8	75% of 2007	1.2	−1.79
15.8%	76	154	80
14.5% and 1.5% 2010 to 2011	70.9%	132	130

MAIN ACTIVITY: REPEATED CHANGE

1. Account A: $500 \times 1.03^5 = £579.64$ Account B: $500 + (0.05 \times 500) \times 5 = £625$ Eric should use account B.
2. Car A: $32500 \times 0.8^4 = £13\,312$ Car B: $27\,000 \times 0.85^4 = £14\,094$ Car B will be worth more.
3. 3 years old

HOMEWORK ACTIVITY: HOW HOT?

1.

19.5 inches	£277.40	415	25% of £60
12.5%	£2120.00	6%	1148.175 m^2
50	£350	60	£60
5 years	£120	£900	£31 250

GLOSSARY

Simple interest
When interest is calculated on the original investment only, not on any interest earned

Compound interest
When interest is calculated on the original investment and any interest earned previously

8 NUMBER: ROUNDING AND ESTIMATION

LEARNING OBJECTIVES

- Apply the four operations, including by using formal written methods
- Estimate answers
- Check calculations using approximation and estimation, including by using technology
- Recognise and use relationships between operations including inverse operations

SPECIFICATION LINKS

- N3, N2, N10, N14, N14, N15, N16

STARTER ACTIVITY

- **What do we know?; 5 minutes; page 60**
  The student is given a long-multiplication calculation and asked to write several facts based on the calculation. You may wish to remind the student of the process of long multiplication before they attempt this starter.

MAIN ACTIVITIES

- **Estimations and error intervals; 25 minutes; page 61**
  Recap how to round a number to a given number of decimal places and significant figures. Establish how to write an error interval for a rounded number using inequality notation (e.g. 3.6 rounded to 1 dp: error interval $3.55 \leq x < 3.65$). Introduce the vocabulary upper and lower bounds.
- **Terminating and recurring decimals; 15 minutes; page 62**
  Before starting this activity, spend some time reinforcing how to change a decimal to a fraction using place value.

PLENARY ACTIVITY

- **How much to carpet the room?; 5 minutes**
  Ask the student to estimate the area of the room you are in to a certain degree of accuracy. Give the cost of underlay (£3.99 per square metre) and carpet (£18.99 per square metre) and ask the student to work out the cost of laying the carpet in the room. Is this an under or overestimate? Ask the student to justify their answer.

HOMEWORK ACTIVITY

- **Exam-style questions; 30 minutes; page 63**
  The student will complete some exam-style questions using the skills covered in this lesson and the previous one.

SUPPORT IDEA

- **Estimations and error intervals** Spend some time rounding decimals and large numbers to a given number of significant figures. Move on to error intervals for rounded numbers before beginning the questions.

EXTENSION IDEA

- **Estimations and error intervals** Extend the idea of estimating and finding exact solutions. Ask the student to work out the percentage error.

PROGRESS AND OBSERVATIONS

STARTER ACTIVITY: WHAT DO WE KNOW?

TIMING: 5 MINS

LEARNING OBJECTIVES

- Recognise and use relationships between operations including inverse operations

EQUIPMENT

Erica works out 325×76 using long multiplication.

```
          ¹   ³
      3   2   5
  ×       7   6
  ─────────────
  1   9   5   0
      ¹   ³
2   2   7   5   0
  ─────────────
      ¹   ¹
2   4   7   0   0
```

1. **Without doing any further calculations, work out the answers to these calculations. Explain to your tutor how you found each answer.**

    a) $325 \times 6 =$ ....

    b) $3.25 \times 76 =$ ....

    c) $24\,700 - 1950 =$ ....

    d) $7.6 \times 3.25 =$ ....

    e) $3250 \times 7.6 =$ ....

MATHS
— HIGHER —

Edexcel

MAIN ACTIVITY: ESTIMATIONS AND ERROR INTERVALS   **TIMING: 25 MINS**

LEARNING OBJECTIVES	EQUIPMENT
• Check calculations using approximation and estimation	• calculator
• Use inequality notation to specify error intervals	

For this activity, use the following values.

$A = 3.04$ $B = 2.78$ $C = 94.8$ $D = 0.405$ $E = 121$

 1. **Find an approximate value for each of these algebraic expressions.**

   a) $2A$ ....

   b) $C - B$ ....

   c) $2D + 3E$ ....

   d) $2(A + E)$ ....

   e) $4A - D$ ....

   f) A^2 ....

   g) $\dfrac{A}{D}$ ....

   h) $\dfrac{A - E}{2}$ ....

   i) $A - B \times C$ ....

   j) $\sqrt{E} - 2C$ ....

2. **Given that the values have been rounded to 3 significant figures, work out the maximum and minimum values of each expression. Then give the error interval for each expression. Write your answers on the lines above.**

MAIN ACTIVITY: TERMINATING AND RECURRING DECIMALS   TIMING: 15 MINS

LEARNING OBJECTIVES	EQUIPMENT
• Convert fractions into decimals including recurring decimals • Convert recurring decimals into fractions	• calculator

1. **Complete this calculation to find the decimal value of $\frac{3}{8}$.**

$$8\overline{\smash{)}3.0000}$$

$$\frac{3}{8} = \text{------------------------------------}$$

2. **Convert these fractions into decimals.**

a) $\frac{2}{3}$ ------------------------------------

b) $\frac{5}{9}$ ------------------------------------

c) $\frac{4}{7}$ ------------------------------------

d) $\frac{7}{11}$ ------------------------------------

Example:
Write $0.1\dot{4}\dot{5}$ as a fraction.

$$x = 0.1\dot{4}\dot{5}$$
$$1000x = 145.1\dot{4}\dot{5}$$
$$1000x - x = 145.1\dot{4}\dot{5} - 0.1\dot{4}\dot{5}$$
$$999x = 145$$
$$x = \frac{145}{999}$$

---

3. **Convert these decimals to fractions.**

a) $0.\dot{7}$ ------------------------------------

b) $0.0\dot{6}\dot{7}$ ------------------------------------

c) $0.8\dot{7}$ ------------------------------------

d) $0.\dot{1}0\dot{5}$ ------------------------------------

HOMEWORK ACTIVITY: EXAM-STYLE QUESTIONS   TIMING: 30 MINS

LEARNING OBJECTIVES
- Convert recurring decimals into fractions
- Check calculations using approximation and estimation
- Use inequality notation to specify error intervals
- Find the upper and lower bound in real life situations

EQUIPMENT
- calculator

1. **Emily rounds a number, *m*, to 3 significant figures.**
   The result is 3.47.
   Write an error interval for *m*.

   ....
   (2 marks)

2. **Prove algebraically that $0.0\dot{8} = \dfrac{4}{45}$.**

   ....
   ....
   ....
   ....
   (2 marks)

3. **A rectangular lawn measures 3.5 m by 4.7 m to the nearest 10 cm. Turf costs £2.24 per square metre.**

   Work out an error interval for the total cost of laying the turf. Show all your calculations.

   ....
   ....
   ....
   ....
   (4 marks)

4. **The mass of a piece of gold is 45.2 g. The density of the gold is 19.3 g/cm³.**

   Given that both values are rounded to 1 decimal place, work out the upper bound for the volume of the gold. Give your answer to 3 significant figures.

   ....
   ....
   (3 marks)

8 ANSWERS

STARTER ACTIVITY: WHAT DO WE KNOW?

1. a) 1950   b) 247   c) 22 750   d) 24.7   e) 24 700

MAIN ACTIVITY: ESTIMATIONS AND ERROR INTERVALS

1. a) 6   b) 92   c) 360.8   d) 248   e) 11.6
f) 9   g) 7   h) −59   i) −260   j) −179

2. a) $6.07 \leq 2A < 6.09$ b) $91.965 \leq C - B < 92.075$ c) $362.309 \leq 2D + 3E < 365.311$

d) $247.07 \leq 2(A + E) < 249.09$ e) $11.7345 \leq 4A - D < 11.7755$ f) $9.211225 \leq A^2 < 9.272025$

g) $7.48458693 \leq \dfrac{A}{D} < 7.527812114$ h) $-59.2325 \leq \dfrac{A - E}{2} < -58.7275$ i) $-261.12225 \leq A - B \times C < -259.88625$

j) $-178.7227508 \leq \sqrt{E} - 2C < -178.4772962$

MAIN ACTIVITY: TERMINATING AND RECURRING DECIMALS

1. 0.375

2. a) $0.\dot{6}$ b) $0.\dot{5}$ c) $0.\dot{5}7142\dot{8}$ d) $0.6\dot{3}$

3. a) $\dfrac{7}{9}$ b) $\dfrac{67}{990}$ c) $\dfrac{79}{90}$ d) $\dfrac{35}{333}$

HOMEWORK ACTIVITY: EXAM-STYLE QUESTIONS

1. $3.465 \leq m < 3.475$

2. $x = 0.0\dot{8}$

   $10x = 0.8\dot{8}$

   $9x = 0.8$

   $x = \dfrac{0.8}{9}$

   $= \dfrac{4}{45}$

3. $(3.45 \times 4.65) \times 2.24 \leq \text{cost} < (3.55 \times 4.75) \times 2.24$

   $£35.94 \leq \text{cost} < £37.77$

4. 2.35 cm^3

GLOSSARY

Upper bound
The value below which all values in a range must lie

Lower bound
The smallest value a rounded value may take

9 ALGEBRA: INTRODUCING ALGEBRA

LEARNING OBJECTIVES

- Use algebraic notation and symbols correctly
- Substitute numerical values into formulae and expressions
- Understand and use concepts and vocabulary of expressions, equations, formulae, identity, terms
- Simplify and manipulate algebraic expressions

SPECIFICATION LINKS

- A1, A2, A3, A4, A5, A6, A7

STARTER ACTIVITY

- **Simplify the expression; 5 minutes; page 66**
  Full instructions are given on the activity sheet.

MAIN ACTIVITIES

- **Algebraic manipulation; 25 minutes; page 67**
  Remind the student that calculating with algebraic terms follows the same conventions as numerical values. Discuss the different terminology associated with algebra: equation, expression, term, formula, identity, simplify, solve, substitute, expand, proof. Look at the first question together and identify any questions that the student finds challenging. Work through these questions at the appropriate level, explaining any techniques required.
- **Functions; 15 minutes; page 68**
  Revise function notation and how to find composite functions and inverse functions.
  The student is required to complete a 'route' through the grid, answering at least one question on each layer.

PLENARY ACTIVITY

- **Three things I've learned; 5 minutes**
  Ask the student to describe three new things they have learned during this lesson. These things may simply be a deepened understanding of topics with which they were already familiar.

HOMEWORK ACTIVITY

- **Terminology; 40 minutes; page 69**
  Full instructions are given on the activity sheet.

SUPPORT IDEA

- **Algebraic manipulation/Functions** When changing the subject of a formula, you may wish to link to functions by drawing out a function machine and using this to support the process.

EXTENSION IDEA

- **Functions** Given an output, challenge the student to find the input of the function. Give a composite function and challenge the student to identify which functions have been combined and how.

PROGRESS AND OBSERVATIONS

STARTER ACTIVITY: SIMPLIFY THE EXPRESSION

TIMING: 5 MINS

LEARNING OBJECTIVES

- Use algebraic notation and symbols correctly

EQUIPMENT

1. Draw lines to match each of the expressions on the left with its equivalent simplified expression on the right. Some of the expressions on the right will match more than one of the expressions on the left.

a) $a + a$

b) $4a^2 \div 2a$

c) $(2a)^2$

d) $\dfrac{4a}{a}$

e) $2a + 2a$

f) $4a \times a$

g) $a \times a$

h) $2 \times a^2$

i) $2a \times 2a$

j) $2a^2 \div a$

k) $4a \div 2$

l) $4a^2 \div 2a^2$

m) $\dfrac{4a^2}{2a^2}$

n) $2a \times a$

o) $2a \times 2$

2

a^2

$2a$

$2a^2$

$4a$

$4a^2$

4

MAIN ACTIVITY: ALGEBRAIC MANIPULATION   TIMING: 25 MINS

LEARNING OBJECTIVES

- Use algebraic notation and symbols correctly
- Substitute numerical values into formulae and expressions
- Understand and use concepts and vocabulary of expressions, equations, formulae, identity, terms
- Simplify and manipulate algebraic expressions

EQUIPMENT

1. **Answer these questions about substitution and formulae.**

   a) Given that $c = \frac{2a}{3d}$, find the value of C when $a = -6$ and $d = 15$. ....

   b) Make n the subject of the formula $n^2 = m + 1$. ....

   c) If $y = 2x + 5$, what is the value of x when $y = 11$? ....

   d) If $y = x^2 + 3$, what is the value of x when $y = 12$? ....

   e) Make v the subject of the equation $d = v^2 + m$. ....

   f) Make m the subject of the formula $x = \frac{1}{m} + 2v$ . ...

2. **Answer these questions about expanding and simplifying expressions.**

   a) Expand and simplify $2(3x + 1) - x$. ....

   b) Expand and simplify $(x + 3)(x - 4)$. ....

   c) Simplify $\frac{2x + 8n}{2}$ . ...

   d) Expand and simplify $(3x - 1)^2$. ....

   e) A square has sides of length $(x + 2)$ cm. Prove that the area of the square is $x^2 + 4x + 4$ cm^2.

   ....

   f) Prove that in the sequence of even numbers, the product of two consecutive terms is always a multiple of 4.

   ....

MATHS
— HIGHER —

Edexcel

MAIN ACTIVITY: FUNCTIONS

TIMING: 15 MINS

LEARNING OBJECTIVES

- Use function notation
- Find composite and inverse functions algebraically

EQUIPMENT

- dice

1. **Roll the dice to move around the board. Answer the questions you land on using the functions below. You must answer the questions on the start and finish squares.**

$f(x) = 2x + 5$ $\qquad$ $g(x) = x^2$ $\qquad$ $h(x) = 10 - 3x$ $\qquad$ $k(x) = \dfrac{2x}{3}$

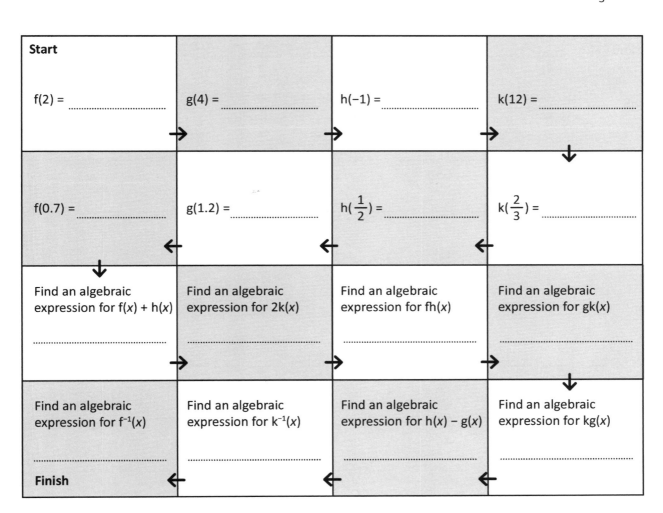

Start			
$f(2) =$ .... $\rightarrow$	$g(4) =$ .... $\rightarrow$	$h(-1) =$ .... $\rightarrow$	$k(12) =$ .... $\downarrow$
$f(0.7) =$ .... $\downarrow$	$g(1.2) =$ .... $\leftarrow$	$h(\frac{1}{2}) =$ .... $\leftarrow$	$k(\frac{2}{3}) =$ .... $\leftarrow$
Find an algebraic expression for $f(x) + h(x)$ .... $\rightarrow$	Find an algebraic expression for $2k(x)$ .... $\rightarrow$	Find an algebraic expression for $fh(x)$ .... $\rightarrow$	Find an algebraic expression for $gk(x)$ .... $\downarrow$
Find an algebraic expression for $f^{-1}(x)$ .... **Finish** $\leftarrow$	Find an algebraic expression for $k^{-1}(x)$ .... $\leftarrow$	Find an algebraic expression for $h(x) - g(x)$ .... $\leftarrow$	Find an algebraic expression for $kg(x)$ ....

HOMEWORK ACTIVITY: TERMINOLOGY

TIMING: 40 MINS

EQUIPMENT

- dictionary (optional)

LEARNING OBJECTIVES

- Understand and use concepts and vocabulary of expressions, equations, formulae, identity, terms, function, inverse, simplify, expand, substitute, proof

1. **Create your own dictionary to define all the algebraic language you have encountered during this lesson.**

   Include an example for each term below.

   expression: ....

   equation: ....

   formula: ....

   identity: ....

   term: ....

   function: ....

   inverse: ....

   simplify: ....

   expand: ....

   substitute: ....

   proof: ....

9 ANSWERS

STARTER ACTIVITY: SIMPLIFY THE EXPRESSION

1. a) $2a$ b) $2a$ c) $4a^2$ d) 4 e) $4a$ f) $4a^2$ g) a^2

h) $2a^2$ i) $4a^2$ j) $2a$ k) $2a$ l) 2 m) 2 n) $2a^2$ o) $4a$

MAIN ACTIVITY: ALGEBRAIC MANIPULATION

1. a) $-\dfrac{4}{15}$ b) $n = \pm\sqrt{m+1}$ c) $x = 3$

d) $x = \pm 3$ e) $v = \pm\sqrt{d-m}$ f) $\dfrac{1}{x-2v}$

2. a) $5x + 2$ b) $x^2 - x - 12$ c) $x + 4n$

d) $9x^2 - 6x + 1$

e) $(x+2)(x+2) = x^2 + 2x + 2x + 4$
$\qquad\qquad\quad = x^2 + 4x + 4$

f) $2n(2n+2) = 4n^2 + 4n$
$\qquad\qquad\ = 4(n^2 + n)$

MAIN ACTIVITY: FUNCTIONS

1.

9	16	13	8
6.4	1.44	$8\frac{1}{2}$	4
$15 - x$	$\dfrac{4x}{3}$	$25 - 6x$	$\dfrac{4x^2}{9}$
$\dfrac{x-5}{2}$	$\dfrac{3x}{2}$	$10 - 3x - x^2$	$\dfrac{2x^2}{3}$

HOMEWORK ACTIVITY: TERMINOLOGY

1. See the glossary. Check the student's examples.

GLOSSARY

Equation
A statement that two mathematical statements are equal

Expand
To multiply out brackets

Expression
The sum of two or more algebraic terms

Formula
A relationship between two or more variables

Function
A relationship between a set of inputs and a set of outputs

Identity
A statement that two mathematical statements are always equal

Inequality
A statement that two mathematical statements are not equal

Inverse
The opposite function

Proof
An argument that establishes a fact

Simplify
To collect together like terms

Substitute
To replace algebraic values with numeric values

Term
A single number or variable or product of a number and variable

10 ALGEBRA: SOLVING LINEAR EQUATIONS

LEARNING OBJECTIVES

- Solve linear equations in one unknown algebraically
- Set up and solve linear equations

SPECIFICATION LINKS

- A1, A2, A3, A4, A17

STARTER ACTIVITY

- **Smallest value; 5 minutes; page 72**
  Full instructions are given on the activity sheet.

MAIN ACTIVITIES

- **Solving equations; 25 minutes; page 73**
  Discuss the meaning of the word 'equation', and how it differs from formula, term or expression. Establish the concept of balancing the sides by carrying out the same action to both sides of an equation. Reinforce that to solve an equation, you must collect like terms first before carrying out inverse operations.
- **Problem solving using algebra; 15 minutes; page 74**
  This activity requires the student to apply the skills covered in *Solving equations*.

PLENARY ACTIVITY

- **Substitute, simplify, solve?; 5 minutes**
  Ask the student to draw a mind map of all the algebraic techniques learned so far. Encourage the student to identify the areas of algebra they find most challenging.

HOMEWORK ACTIVITY

- **Write your own test; 40 minutes; page 75**
  Full instructions are given on the activity sheet. However, you may wish to adjust the challenge level to suit the student by changing the value of *x*.

SUPPORT IDEA

- **Solving equations** When solving equations, draw a pair of old-fashioned scales. Help the student to grasp that the equals sign indicates balance. Establish that to maintain this balance, the same must be added or subtracted to both sides of the scales, or equation. Make sure the student is aware that this also applies to multiplication and division.

EXTENSION IDEA

- **Problem solving using algebra** Invite the student to design their own problem-solving questions that result in a given equation to solve (e.g. $3x + 4 = 7x - 36$).

PROGRESS AND OBSERVATIONS

STARTER ACTIVITY: SMALLEST VALUE

TIMING: 5 MINS

LEARNING OBJECTIVES

- Substitute values into algebraic expressions

EQUIPMENT

1. Given that $y = 3(x + 5)^2 - 20$, what is the value of y when:

   a) $x = 1$ ....

   b) $x = 0$ ....

   c) $x = -10$ ....

2. What is the smallest value that *y* could be? Explain how you know this.

....

....

....

MAIN ACTIVITY: SOLVING EQUATIONS

TIMING: 25 MINS

LEARNING OBJECTIVES

- Solve linear equations in one unknown, algebraically

EQUIPMENT

- red, orange and green coloured pencils

1. Challenge yourself to see how many of these equations you can solve in 25 minutes. Make sure you answer at least one question on every row. Colour each square to show how difficult you found it – green for easy, orange for average, red for difficult.

Unknown on one side	$2x - 3 = 7$	$3(x - 2) = -18$	$\dfrac{3x}{2} = 9$	$-3 = \dfrac{x+4}{2}$	$\dfrac{2(x+5)}{5} = 4\dfrac{4}{5}$
Unknown on both sides	$\dfrac{z+14}{4} = 2z$	$2(3x + 1) = 10 - 5x$	$4x - 3 = 1 - 4x$	$3x + 1 = -2(5x - 7)$	$4x - 7 = x + 4$
Squared unknown	$x^2 + 1 = 17$	$2(x^2 - 5) = -8$	$10 = \dfrac{x^2}{12}$	$3x^2 + 2x = 2x + 100$	$3x^2 = 10 - 2x^2$
Fractions	$\dfrac{1}{4}x + 12 = \dfrac{3}{5}x + 5$	$\dfrac{3}{4}x^2 = 5$	$\dfrac{2}{3}(x - 4) = -2$	$\dfrac{x+5}{10} = \dfrac{2x-24}{3}$	$\dfrac{3(10-x)}{9} = \dfrac{-2(x-5)}{4}$

MAIN ACTIVITY: PROBLEM SOLVING USING ALGEBRA   **TIMING: 15 MINS**

LEARNING OBJECTIVES

- Set up and solve linear equations

EQUIPMENT

1. **In a bookshop, fiction books cost £3 less than non-fiction books.**
   The cost of a fiction book is £F.

   a) Write an expression for the cost of a non-fiction book.

   ----

   b) The cost of one non-fiction book and one fiction book is £21. Form and solve an equation to work out the cost of each book.

   ----

2. **Here is a rectangle.**

   a) Write and simplify an expression for the perimeter of the rectangle.

   $3x + 1$ cm

   $x - 3$ cm

   The perimeter of the rectangle is 36 cm.

   b) Create and solve an equation to find the value of x.

   ----

   c) Work out the area of the rectangle.

   ----

3. **In a triangle, the angles are in the ratio 3 : 4 : 5. Form and solve an equation to work out the size of the smallest angle.**

   ----

4. **A square has sides of length x.**
   The largest circle possible is drawn inside the square so that the circumference of the circle touches all four sides of the square.

   x cm

   The area of the shaded section is 10.5 cm^2 to 1 decimal place.
   Work out the length of x, giving your answer to the nearest centimetre.

HOMEWORK ACTIVITY: WRITE YOUR OWN TEST   TIMING: **40** MINS

LEARNING OBJECTIVES

- Solve linear equations in one unknown algebraically
- Set up and solve linear equations

EQUIPMENT

When writing equations questions to solve, an examiner often works backwards. They might start with the solution and then form two algebraic expressions that would have the same value.

For example, if the value of x was 6, all the following expressions would have the same value:

$2x + 4$ $x + 10$ $x^2 - 20$ $\dfrac{x}{3} + 14$ $2(3x - 10)$

The examiner could then choose any two and set them equal to each other. This would give an equation to solve.

For example, $2x + 4 = \dfrac{x}{3} + 14$.

1. **Create 10 equations to solve. Each equation should give the solution $x = -3$. Make sure you only use each expression for x once.**

   Try to include fractional values, squares, brackets and negative numbers. Make your questions as complex as you can!

----

10 ANSWERS

STARTER ACTIVITY: SMALLEST VALUE

1. a) $y = 88$ b) $y = 55$ c) $y = 55$

2. Smallest value of y is -20. This occurs when $x = -5$ since the smallest value that a square number can take is 0.

MAIN ACTIVITY: SOLVING EQUATIONS

1.

Unknown on one side	$x = 5$	$x = -4$	$x = 6$	$x = -10$	$x = 7$
Unknown on both sides	$z = 2$	$x = \dfrac{8}{11}$	$x = \dfrac{1}{2}$	$x = 1$	$x = 3\dfrac{2}{3}$
Squared unknown	$x = \pm 4$	$x = \pm 1$	$x = \pm 2\sqrt{30}$	$x = \pm\dfrac{10\sqrt{3}}{3}$	$x = \pm\sqrt{2}$
Fractions	$x = 20$	$x = \pm\dfrac{2\sqrt{15}}{3}$	$x = 1$	$x = 15$	$x = -5$

MAIN ACTIVITY: PROBLEM SOLVING USING ALGEBRA

1. a) $F + 3$ b) $2F + 3 = 21$ $F = 9$ fiction = £9   non-fiction = £12

2. a) $8x - 4$ b) $8x - 4 = 36$, $x = 5$ c) 32 cm²

3. $12x = 180$, $x = 15$, $3 \times 15 = 45°$

4. $x = 7$ cm

HOMEWORK ACTIVITY: WRITE YOUR OWN TEST

1. Check the student's answers.

GLOSSARY

Equation

A statement saying that two mathematical statements are equal

11 ALGEBRA: SOLVING QUADRATIC EQUATIONS

LEARNING OBJECTIVES

- Factorise a quadratic equation
- Write a quadratic equation in completed square form
- Solve quadratic equations by factorising
- Solve quadratic equations by completing the square
- Solve quadratic equations using the quadratic formula

SPECIFICATION LINKS

- A1, A2, A3, A4, A18

STARTER ACTIVITY

- **Algebraic terminology; 5 minutes; page 78**
  Full instructions are given on the activity sheet.

MAIN ACTIVITIES

- **Manipulating quadratic expressions; 25 minutes; page 79**
  Some students may need more practice with factorising quadratic expressions. If so, ask the student to complete all parts of question 3 rather than as many as they can in the given time.
- **Solving quadratic equations; 15 minutes; page 80**
  Show the student the three ways in which a quadratic equation can be solved by working through the examples on the activity sheet. Discuss when the student might use each method. Add that sometimes, an exam question will specify the method to use, so it is important to be competent in all three methods. Ask the student to follow the instructions on the activity sheet.

PLENARY ACTIVITY

- **Pros and cons; 5 minutes**
  Ask the student to list the pros and cons of each method for solving a quadratic equation, and to explain how they might identify which method to use.

HOMEWORK ACTIVITY

- **How to …; 40 minutes; page 81**
  Full instructions are given on the activity sheet.

SUPPORT IDEA

- **Manipulating quadratic expressions** Ask the student to list the possible pairs of factors of the numeric term and the coefficient of x^2 before attempting to factorise. You may also wish to give the student one of the values in the factorised expression, e.g. $6x^2 + 13x + 5 = (2x \ldots)(\ldots)$.

EXTENSION IDEA

- **Manipulating quadratic expressions** Challenge the student to make x the subject of the equation $x^2 + bx + c = 0$ by completing the square. Then move on to $ax^2 + bx + c = 0$ to reach the quadratic formula.

PROGRESS AND OBSERVATIONS

MATHS
— HIGHER —

Edexcel

STARTER ACTIVITY: ALGEBRAIC TERMINOLOGY

TIMING: 5 MINS

LEARNING OBJECTIVES

- Understand and use the concepts and vocabulary of expressions, equations, formulae, identities, inequalities and terms

EQUIPMENT

1. **Choose a word from the cloud to describe each of the following.**

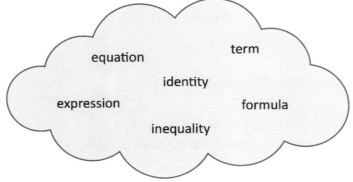

equation   term
identity
expression   formula
inequality

a) $2x + 4$ ....

b) $y = mx + c$ ....

c) $3a$ ....

d) $4x \equiv x + x + x + x$ ....

e) $4 < 2x + 5$ ....

f) $2x - 5 = 17$ ....

MAIN ACTIVITY: MANIPULATING QUADRATIC EXPRESSIONS   TIMING: 25 MINS

LEARNING OBJECTIVES
- Factorise a quadratic equation
- Write a quadratic equation in completed square form

EQUIPMENT
none

 1. $x^2 - 3x - 10$

    a) Without expanding the brackets, identify the correct factorisation of the above expression.

          A: $(x-3)(x+1)$ B: $(x-10)(x+1)$ C: $(x-5)(x-2)$ D: $(x-5)(x+2)$ E: $(x-2)(x+5)$

    b) Explain how you know.

----

2. $(2x+5)(3x-7)$

    a) Expand the brackets and simplify your answer into the form $ax^2 + bx + c$.

----

    b) Explain what you notice about the relationship between the numerical values in $(2x+5)(3x-7)$ and the value a, b and c.

----

 3. **Factorise and solve as many of these expressions as you can in ten minutes.**

    a) $x^2 - x - 12$ ....   b) $6x^2 - 35x - 6$ ....

    c) $x^2 - 12x + 35$ ....   d) $10x^2 - x - 2$ ....

    e) $6x^2 + 13x + 5$ ....   f) $x^2 - 16$ ....

    g) $8x^2 - 16x + 6$ ....   h) $4x^2 - 25$ ....

> **Example:**
> Find the values of a, b and c in $2x^2 + 12x - 8 = a(x+b)^2 - c$.
> $$2x^2 + 12x - 8 = 2(x^2 + 6x - 4)$$
> $$= 2(x+3)^2 - 9 - 4$$
> $$= 2(x+3)^2 - 13$$
> $$= 2(x+3)^2 - 26$$
> so $a = 2$, $b = 3$, $c = 26$.

4. **Write each of these expressions in completed square form.**

    a) $x^2 + 6x + 5$ ....   b) $2x^2 + 8x - 16$ ....

    c) $3x^2 - 9x + 12$ ....

MATHS
— HIGHER —

Edexcel

MAIN ACTIVITY: SOLVING QUADRATIC EQUATIONS

TIMING: 15 MINS

LEARNING OBJECTIVES

- Solve quadratic equations by factorising
- Solve quadratic equations by completing the square
- Solve quadratic equations using the quadratic formula

EQUIPMENT

There are three ways to solve quadratic equations.
For all three methods, first rearrange the quadratic equation into the form $ax^2 + bx + c = 0$.
For example: $2x^2 - 5x = 12$ would rearrange to $2x^2 - 5x - 12 = 0$.

Method 1: Factorise	Method 2: Complete the square	Method 3: The quadratic formula
$2x^2 - 5x - 12 = 0$ $(2x+3)(x-4) = 0$ $2x+3=0$ or $x-4=0$ $x = -\dfrac{3}{2}$ or $x = 4$	$2x^2 - 5x - 12 = 0$ $x^2 - \dfrac{5}{2}x - 6 = 0$ (divide by 2) $\left(x - \dfrac{5}{4}\right)^2 - \dfrac{25}{16} - 6 = 0$ $\left(x - \dfrac{5}{4}\right)^2 - \dfrac{121}{16} = 0$ $\left(x - \dfrac{5}{4}\right)^2 = \dfrac{121}{16}$ $\left(x - \dfrac{5}{4}\right) = \pm\dfrac{11}{4}$ $x = \pm\dfrac{11}{4} + \dfrac{5}{4}$ $x = 4$ or $x = -\dfrac{3}{2}$	$x = \dfrac{-b \pm \sqrt{b^2 - 4ac}}{2a}$ $2x^2 - 5x - 12 = 0$ $a = 2, \ b = -5, \ c = -12$ $x = \dfrac{5 \pm \sqrt{-5^2 - 4 \times 2 \times -12}}{2}$ $= \dfrac{5 \pm \sqrt{25 + 96}}{4}$ $= \dfrac{5 \pm \sqrt{121}}{4}$ $x = 4$ or $x = -\dfrac{3}{2}$

1. **Choose one of the methods above to find the exact solution to each of these quadratic equations.**
   Explain why you chose the method you did. Try to use each method at least once.

   a) $2x^2 - 5x - 25 = 0$ ....

   ....

   b) $x^2 + 6(x + 1) = 0$ ....

   ....

   c) $3x^2 + 1 = 6x$ ....

   ....

   d) $3x^2 = 2x + 3$ ....

   ....

MATHS
— HIGHER —

HOMEWORK ACTIVITY: HOW TO ...

TIMING: 40 MINS

LEARNING OBJECTIVES

- Solve quadratic equations by factorising
- Solve quadratic equations by completing the square
- Solve quadratic equations using the quadratic formula

EQUIPMENT

1. **Make your own instructions for solving quadratic equations. Make a video, booklet or poster to explain the three ways of solving a quadratic equation.**

   Remember to include the following methods:

   - Solving by factorising
   - Solving by completing the square
   - Solving using the quadratic formula

   Ensure that you include a new example for each method, showing how it can be used.

11 ANSWERS

STARTER ACTIVITY: ALGEBRAIC TERMINOLOGY

1. a) expression   b) formula   c) term
   d) identity   e) inequality   f) equation

MAIN ACTIVITY: MANIPULATING QUADRATIC EXPRESSIONS

1. a) D   b) The product of the numeric terms is -10 and $-5 + 2 = -3$

2. a) $6x^2 + x - 35$
   b) 6 is the product of 2 and 3; 1 is the sum of 2×-7 and 5×3; -35 is the product of 5 and -7

3. a) $(x + 3)(x - 4)$ b) $(6x + 1)(x - 6)$ c) $(x - 7)(x - 5)$ d $(2x - 1)(5x + 2)$
   e) $(2x + 1)(3x + 5)$ f) $(x - 4)(x + 4)$ g) $(2x - 3)(4x - 2)$ h) $(2x - 5)(2x + 5)$

4. a) $(x + 3)^2 - 4$ b) $2(x + 2)^2 - 24$ c) $3\left(x - \dfrac{3}{2}\right)^2 - \dfrac{21}{4}$

MAIN ACTIVITY: SOLVING QUADRATIC EQUATIONS

a) Factorise to give $(2x + 5)(x - 5)$ giving $x = -\dfrac{5}{2}$ or $x = 5$

b) Complete the square to give $(x + 3)^2 - 3 = 0$, giving $x = -3 \pm \sqrt{3}$

c) Use the quadratic formula to give: $3(x - 1)^2 - 2 = 0$, giving $x = 1 \pm \sqrt{\dfrac{2}{3}}$

d) Choose a method to find the exact solution to give: $x = \dfrac{1}{3} \pm \dfrac{1}{3}\sqrt{10}$

HOMEWORK ACTIVITY: HOW TO ...

1. Student's own work. Check the explanations and examples are correct.

GLOSSARY

Quadratic equation
An algebraic equation in which the highest power of x is x^2

12 ALGEBRA: SIMULTANEOUS EQUATIONS

LEARNING OBJECTIVES

- Solve two simultaneous equations in two variables (linear/linear and linear/quadratic) algebraically and graphically

SPECIFICATION LINKS

- A1, A2, A3, A4, A5, A9, A12, A19, A21

STARTER ACTIVITY

- **If I know... then what else do I know?; 5 minutes; page 84**
  Full instructions are given on the activity sheet.

MAIN ACTIVITIES

- **Solving simultaneous equations algebraically; 25 minutes; page 85**
  Work through the two methods for solving simultaneous equations. Ask the student whether they prefer the elimination method or the substitution method. Then ask the student to work through the questions on the activity sheet.
  Explain that the student could check or solve simultaneous equations using a graphical method.

- **Problem solving with simultaneous equations; 15 minutes; page 86**
  These questions require the student to apply the skills they covered in the first part of the lesson. Encourage the student to highlight the key information and to form equations where necessary in order to solve the problems. Stress that trial and improvement techniques will not achieve any marks. Encourage the student to check solutions by substituting into the original equations.

PLENARY ACTIVITY

- **If I know... then what else do I know?; 5 minutes**
  Refer the student back to the starter activity and discuss how equations can be manipulated. Establish that if they carry out the same operation to both sides of an equation, it remains true. Discuss with the student how they have used this principal when solving simultaneous equations.

HOMEWORK ACTIVITY

- **All about simultaneous equations; 60 minutes; page 87**
  Full instructions are given on the activity sheet.

SUPPORT IDEA

- **Solving simultaneous equations algebraically** Before working on questions 1 and 2, invite the student to think about how to eliminate one unknown. Establish that if the signs are different they should add, but if the signs are the same, they should subtract. You may wish to illustrate this with 'balance scales' to help the student to visualise this.

EXTENSION IDEA

- **Solving simultaneous equations algebraically** Invite the student to design their own pair of simultaneous equations to solve. Challenge the student to make it a pair of simultaneous equations that you could solve by elimination or substitution.

PROGRESS AND OBSERVATIONS

STARTER ACTIVITY: IF I KNOW... THEN WHAT ELSE DO I KNOW?   TIMING: 5 MINS

LEARNING OBJECTIVES

- Manipulate algebraic expressions

EQUIPMENT

1. If you know that $a^2 + b = 12$, which of these equations must also be true?
   Write true or false next to each equation.

   a) $2a^2 + 2b = 24$ ....

   b) $a^2 + 12 = b$ ....

   c) $a^2 = b - 12$ ....

   d) $b = 12 - a^2$ ....

   e) $b = a^2 - 12$ ....

   f) $b = \pm\sqrt{12} - b$ ....

MAIN ACTIVITY: SOLVING SIMULTANEOUS EQUATIONS ALGEBRAICALLY TIMING: 25 MINS

LEARNING OBJECTIVES	EQUIPMENT
• Solve two simultaneous equations in two variables	• plain paper

There are two ways in which to solve linear simultaneous equations such as: $3x - y = 14$
$5x + y = 26$

Method 1: Elimination	Method 2: Substitution
Adding the equations together gives: $3x - y = 14$ $\underline{5x + y = 26}$ $8x = 40$ $x = 5$ Substitute $x = 5$ into either equation: $(3 \times 5) - y = 14$ $y = 1$ Therefore $x = 5$, $y = 1$.	Rearrange $3x - y = 14$ to make y the subject: $y = 3x - 14$ Substitute for y into the 2nd equation: $5x + (3x - 14) = 26$ $8x - 14 = 26$ Solve for x: $8x = 40$ $x = 5$ Substitute $x = 5$ into either equation: $(3 \times 5) - y = 14$ $y = 1$ Therefore $x = 5$, $y = 1$.

1. Solve these simultaneous equations using the method you prefer. Show your working on a separate piece of paper.

   a) $x + y = 19$
      $x - y = 1$

   b) $3x + y = 5$
      $x + y = 1$

   c) $2x + 3y = 18$
      $x + 3y = 15$

   ----------------------------------   ----------------------------------   ----------------------------------

2. Solve these simultaneous equations. You will need to multiply one of the equations first to make the same number of 'x' or 'y'.

   a) $3x + y = 13$
      $x + 3y = 23$

   b) $x - y = 7$
      $3x - 2y = 19$

   c) $x + y = -5$
      $2x + 3y = -13$

   ----------------------------------   ----------------------------------   ----------------------------------

3. $x^2 + y^2 = 29$
   $2x + y = 9$

   a) Explain why you cannot use elimination to solve these simultaneous equations.

   ----

   b) The second equation is rearranged to make y the subject: $y = 9 - 2x$
      Then the expression for y is substituted into the first equation: $x^2 + (9 - 2x)^2 = 29$

      Expand and simplify the quadratic equation.   --

   c) Solve the quadratic to find the values of x.   --

   d) Find the values of y and check your answers by substituting into the original equation.

MAIN ACTIVITY: PROBLEM SOLVING WITH SIMULTANEOUS EQUATIONS TIMING: 15 MINS

LEARNING OBJECTIVES	EQUIPMENT
• Solve two simultaneous equations in two variables and find approximate solutions using graphs	• graph paper

1. **Two different window cleaning companies charge different rates:**

   Clean All: £20 per building + £2 per window   Windowlux: £4 per window.

   This graph illustrates Windowlux's rates for one building.

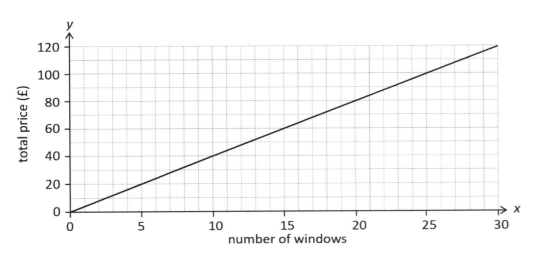

   a)   On the same axis, draw a graph to represent Clean All's rates for one building.

   b)   Use the graph to work out the minimum number of windows you would have to clean to make it cheaper with Clean All. Explain your method to your tutor.

----

2. **Two cups of tea and one coffee cost £6.50. Three cups of tea and two coffees cost £11.10. How much would one cup of tea and one coffee cost?**

----

3. **Follow the instructions below to solve the pair of simultaneous equations.**

   a)   On a sheet of graph paper, sketch the graph of $y = x^2 + 2$.

   b)   On the same axis, sketch the graph of $y = x + 4$.

   c)   Find the solution to the simultaneous equations $y = x^2 + 2$ and $y = x + 4$. Explain your method.

HOMEWORK ACTIVITY: ALL ABOUT SIMULTANEOUS EQUATIONS   TIMING: 60 MINS

LEARNING OBJECTIVES	EQUIPMENT
• Solve two simultaneous equations in two variables	• graph paper

1. The menu on a menu board in a restaurant has been partly obscured.
   However, the waiter knows that 2 curries and 1 rice cost £15.00, but 3 curries and 3 rice cost £25.50.

   What would be the bill for 1 curry and 1 rice?

---

2. From the list of equations below, choose any pair and solve them simultaneously. What do you notice?

   $2a + b = 1$ $a = b - 4$ $3a = -b$ $a^2 + b^2 = 10$ $b = a^2 + 2$

---

3. Solve these simultaneous equations by plotting them onto graphs. Check your answers algebraically.

   a) $y = -2x + 1$, $y = 4x + 4$

   ---

   b) $y = 2x - 5$, $y = x$

   ---

   c) $y = x^2 + x$, $y = 15 - x$

12 ANSWERS

STARTER ACTIVITY: IF I KNOW... THEN WHAT ELSE DO I KNOW?

1. a) and d) are true.

MAIN ACTIVITY: SOLVING SIMULTANEOUS EQUATIONS ALGEBRAICALLY

1. a) $x = 10$, $y = 9$ b) $x = 2$, $y = -1$ c) $x = 3$, $y = 4$
2. a) $x = 2$, $y = 7$ b) $x = 5$, $y = -2$ c) $x = -2$, $y = -3$
3. a) In one equation, the unknowns are squared; in the other equation, they are linear.

b) $x^2 + 81 - 18x - 18x + 4x^2 = 29$ $5x^2 - 36x + 52 = 0$

c) $x = 2$ or 5.2 d) $y = 5$ or -1.4

MAIN ACTIVITY: PROBLEM SOLVING WITH SIMULTANEOUS EQUATIONS

1. a)

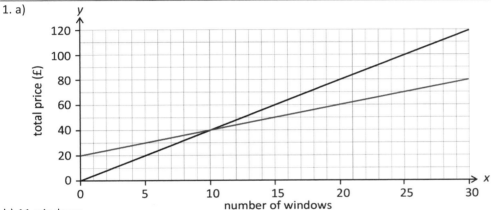

b) 11 windows

2) £4.60

3) Check student's graphs. $x = 2$, $y = 6$, $x = -1$, $y = 3$

HOMEWORK ACTIVITY: ALL ABOUT SIMULTANEOUS EQUATIONS

1. £8.50
2. They all have the same solution $a = -1$, $b = 3$.

$2a + b = 1$ $a = b - 4$	$2a + b = 1$ $3a = -b$	$2a + b = 1$ $a^2 + b^2$ $= 10$	$2a + b = 1$ $b = a^2 + 2$	$a = b - 4$ $3a = -b$	$a = b - 4$ $a^2 + b^2$ $= 10$	$a = b - 4$ $b = a^2 + 2$	$3a = -b$ $a^2 + b^2$ $= 10$	$3a = -b$ $b = a^2 + 2$	$a^2 + b^2$ $= 10$ $b = a^2 + 2$
$a = -1$ $b = 3$	$a = -1$ $b = 3$	$a = -1$ $b = 3$ or $a = 1.8$ $b = -2.6$	$a = -1$ $b = 3$	$a = -1$ $b = 3$	$a = -1$ $b = 3$ or $a = -3$ $b = 1$	$a = -1$ $b = 3$ or $a = 2$ $b = 6$	$a = -1$ $b = 3$ or $a = 1$ $b = -3$	$a = -1$ $b = 3$ or $a = -2$ $b = 6$	$a = 1$ $b = 3$ or $a = -1$ $b = 3$

3. Check student's graphs.

a) $x = -0.5$, $y = 2$ b) $x = 5$, $y = 5$ c) $x = -5$, $y = 20$ or $x = 3$, $y = 12$

GLOSSARY

Simultaneous equations
Equations involving two or more unknowns

13 ALGEBRA: ITERATION

LEARNING OBJECTIVES

- Find approximate solutions to equations numerically using iteration

SPECIFICATION LINKS

- A4, A5, A7, A8, A11, A12, A20

STARTER ACTIVITIES

- **Rearrange; 5 minutes; page 90**
  Full instructions are given on the activity sheet.

MAIN ACTIVITIES

- **Solutions to equations; 15 minutes; page 91**
  Work through the questions on the activity sheet. Explain to the student that the root of an equation is the point where it crosses the x-axis (where $y = 0$). Establish there are two ways in which to identify the two points between which a solution lies: graphically and algebraically.

- **Iterative solutions; 25 minutes; page 92**
  For question 3, show the student how to use the 'ANS' key on their calculator in place of the x_n, making iterative processes easier in a calculation.

PLENARY ACTIVITY

- **Which iterative equation works?; 5 minutes**

  The equation $x^3 + 2x = 5$ can be rearranged to give both: $x = \dfrac{5}{x^2 + 2}$ and $x = \sqrt[3]{-2x + 5}$.

  Using $x_0 = 1$, which iterative formula converges more quickly?

HOMEWORK ACTIVITY

- **Exam-style questions; 20 minutes; page 93**
  Full instructions are given on the activity sheet.

SUPPORT IDEA

- **Iterative solutions** Rearrange the equation $x^3 + 15 = -2x^2$ into the form $x^3 + 15 + 2x^2 = 0$ and plot the graph.
  Support the iterative process by drawing up a table of values for x_0, x_1, etc.

EXTENSION IDEA

- **Iterative solutions** Challenge the student to identify what went wrong with each incorrect rearrangement in question 2.

  Ask the student what would happen if they used the equation $x = -\dfrac{15}{x^2} + 2$ as their iterative formula.

PROGRESS AND OBSERVATIONS

STARTER ACTIVITY: REARRANGE

TIMING: 5 MINS

LEARNING OBJECTIVES

- Rearrange an equation

EQUIPMENT

1. Rearrange each of these equations to make x the subject.

a) $y = 2x + 5$

---

b) $y = x^2 - 6$

---

c) $y - 4x = 2y^2 + 8y$

MAIN ACTIVITY: SOLUTIONS TO EQUATIONS

TIMING: 15 MINUTES

LEARNING OBJECTIVES

- Find approximate solutions to equations numerically and graphically

EQUIPMENT

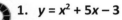 **1.** $y = x^2 + 5x - 3$

a) Complete this table of values for the equation given.

x	−6	−5	−4	−3	−2	−1	0	1	2
y									

b) Plot the points on the axes and sketch the graph of $y = x^2 + 5x - 3$.

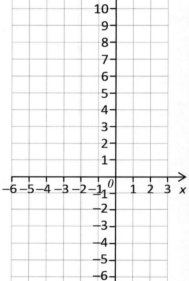

c) Explain why the graph shows that the two solutions to the equation $0 = x^2 + 5x - 3$ lie between −6 and −5 and 0 and 1 on the x-axis.

----

2. Given that f(x) = x^3 + 2x + 5, find the value of each of the following.

a) f(2) = _____

b) f(1) = _____

c) f(0) = _____

d) f(−1) = _____

e) f(−2) = _____

3. The solution to $x^3 + 2x + 5 = 0$ lies between two values for x. What are they? Explain how you know.

MAIN ACTIVITY: ITERATIVE SOLUTIONS

TIMING: 25 MINS

LEARNING OBJECTIVES
- Find approximate solutions to equations numerically using iteration

EQUIPMENT
- scissors

1. Find two whole number values between which the solution to $x^3 + 15 = -2x^2$ lies.

----

2. Which of the following are correct rearrangements of the equation $x^3 + 2x^2 + 15 = 0$?
   Circle the correct equations and show how they have been rearranged.

$$x^3 = 2x^2 + 15 \qquad x = \frac{-2x^2 - 15}{x^2} \qquad x^2 = 2x - 15 \qquad x^2 = \frac{-x^3 - 15}{2} \qquad x = \frac{-15}{x^2 + 2x}$$

----

3. Use the equation $x_{n+1} = \sqrt[3]{-15 - 2x^2}$ and one of the whole number values from question 1 as x_0.

   a) Find the solution to the equation $x^3 + 2x^2 + 15 = 0$ to 2 decimal places.

----

   b) Do you get the same answer using the other numeric value from question 1?

----

4. Below are the parts of a flow chart explaining how to solve an equation iteratively. Cut out the steps and put them in the correct order.

| Find the values of x_1, x_2, x_3… until the desired level of accuracy is achieved. | Find two values between which the solution lies, either graphically or algebraically. | Substitute a starting value into the iterative formula as the value of x_0. | Rearrange the equation into an iterative formula. |

92

HOMEWORK ACTIVITY: EXAM-STYLE QUESTIONS

TIMING: 20 MINS

LEARNING OBJECTIVES

- Find approximate solutions to equations numerically using iteration

EQUIPMENT

1. $x^3 + 5x = 4$

   a) Show that the equation has a solution between $x = 0$ and $x = 1$.

   (2 marks)

   b) Show that the equation can be rearranged to give $x = \dfrac{4}{x^2 + 5}$.

   (2 marks)

   c) Starting with $x = 1$, use the iterative formula $x_{n+1} = \dfrac{4}{x_0^2 + 5}$ to find the solution to $x^3 + 5x = 4$ to three decimal places.

   (3 marks)

2. $f(x) = x^3 + 4x^2 + 5$

   a) Show that the root of the equation $f(x)$ lies between -5 and -4.

   (2 marks)

   b) Using the iterative equation $x_{n+1} = -\dfrac{5}{x_n^2} - 4$ and the starting point $x_0 = -4$, find the values of x_1, x_2 and x_3.

   (3 marks)

13 ANSWERS

STARTER ACTIVITY: REARRANGE

1. a) $x = \dfrac{y-5}{2}$ b) $x = \pm\sqrt{y+6}$ c) $x = \dfrac{-7y-2y^2}{4}$

MAIN ACTIVITY: SOLUTIONS TO EQUATIONS

1. a)

x	−6	−5	−4	−3	−2	−1	0	1	2
y	3	−3	−7	−9	−9	−7	−3	3	11

b)

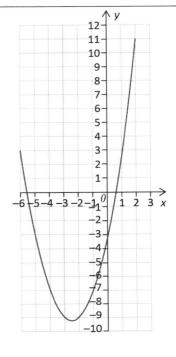

c) The graph crosses the x-axis between these two pairs of points.

2). a) f(2) = 17   b) f(1) = 8   c) f(0) = 5
   d) f(−1) = 2   e) f(−2) = −7

3. −1 and −2: the value of f(x) moves from positive to negative.

MAIN ACTIVITY: ITERATIVE SOLUTIONS

1. −3 and −4

2. $x = \dfrac{-2x^2-15}{x^2}$ $x^2 = \dfrac{-x^3-15}{2}$ $x = \dfrac{-15}{x^2-2x}$

3. a) −3.34   b) yes

4.

Find two values between which the solution lies, either graphically or algebraically.	Rearrange the equation into an iterative formula.	Substitute a starting value into the iterative formula as the value of x_0.	Find the values of x_1, x_2, x_3... until the desired level of accuracy is achieved.

HOMEWORK ACTIVITY: EXAM-STYLE QUESTIONS

1. a) When $x = 0$, $x^3 + 5x = 0 < 4$; when $x = 1$, $x^3 + 5x = 6 > 4$ Therefore the solution lies between 0 and 1.

b) $x^3 + 5x = 4$ $x(x^2 + 5) = 4$ $x = \dfrac{4}{x^2+5}$ c) 0.724

2. a) f(−5) = −20   f(−4) = 5   The value changes from negative to positive, therefore there is a root between −5 and 4.
   b) $x_1 = -4.3125$ $x_2 = -4.2689$ $x_3 = -4.2744$

GLOSSARY

Iterative formula
A mathematical formula that generates a sequence of improving approximate solutions by the previous solution being resubstituted into the formula

14 ALGEBRA: INEQUALITIES

LEARNING OBJECTIVES

- Solve linear inequalities in one variable; represent the solution set on a number line
- Solve inequalities in one or two variables graphically

SPECIFICATION LINKS

- A1, A2, A3, A4, A22

STARTER ACTIVITY

- **Always, sometimes, never; 5 minutes; page 96**
  Full instructions are given on the activity sheet.

MAIN ACTIVITIES

- **Inequalities; 20 minutes; page 97**
  Review the meaning of the four inequality symbols and explain how they can be represented on a number line.
  Model how to solve a linear inequality, linking this to solving linear equations. Discuss why multiplying/dividing both sides of an inequality 'switches' the direction of the inequality sign.
- **Using graphs to solve inequalities; 20 minutes; page 98**
  Model how to solve an inequality by working through the activity. Discuss with the student which areas represent the different inequalities. Encourage them to check their solutions by choosing a particular value of x in the solution set and testing it in the original inequality.

PLENARY ACTIVITY

- **I think of a number; 5 minutes**
  Tell the student that you are thinking of a number. Four more than this number is less than 8. If the number is a positive whole number, what could this number be? (3, 2, 1) Ask the student to create their own question like this for you.

HOMEWORK ACTIVITY

- **Exam-style questions; 25 minutes; page 99**
  Full instructions are given on the activity sheet.

SUPPORT IDEA

- **Inequalities** Encourage the student to make links between solving inequalities and solving equations. Establish that solving linear inequalities is very much like solving linear equations.

EXTENSION IDEA

- **Inequalities** Challenge the student to suggest how you could solve the inequalities in question 4 graphically before moving on.

PROGRESS AND OBSERVATIONS

STARTER ACTIVITY: ALWAYS, SOMETIMES, NEVER   TIMING: 5 MINS

LEARNING OBJECTIVES	EQUIPMENT
• Understand and use the concept and vocabulary of inequalities	none

1. Given that $a \le b$, sort the statements into the table.

Hint: If you are not sure, choose some values that a and b could be and test them. Do not forget that a and b could be positive, negative or zero.

$$a - 5 \le b - 5 \qquad \frac{a}{4} < \frac{b}{4} \qquad b + 3 > a + 3 \qquad a = b$$

$$-a < -b \qquad 4a \le 6b \qquad 5 - b > 10 - a$$

Always true	Sometimes true	Never true

MAIN ACTIVITY: INEQUALITIES   **TIMING: 20 MINS**

LEARNING OBJECTIVES	EQUIPMENT
• Write whole number values that satisfy an inequality	none
• Represent an inequality on a number line	
• Construct an inequality to satisfy a set shown on a number line	
• Solve linear inequalities in one variable; represent the solution set on a number line	

1. **Choose numbers from the cloud that satisfy these inequalities.**

    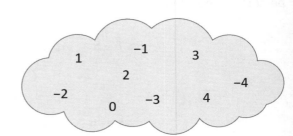

    a) $x > -1$ ....

    b) $-4 < x \leq -2$ ....

    c) $x \geq 0.5$ ....

    d) $-1.1 \leq x \leq 3.4$ ....

2. **Look at these number lines.**

    a) Represent the inequality $-1.5 < b \leq 2.3$.

    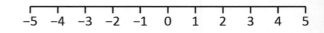

    b) Write the inequality represented on this number line.

    ....

    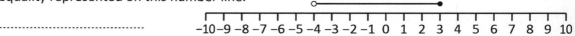

3. **$4 < 5$**

    a) Decide if the inequality will still be true if you:

        i) add any value to both sides ....   ii) divide both sides by a positive number ....

        iii) subtract any value from both sides ....   iv) multiply both sides by a positive number. ....

    b) What happens to the inequality if you:

        i) multiply both sides by a negative number ....

        ii) divide both sides by a negative number. ....

4. **Solve each of these inequalities:**

    a) $3x + 4 > 25$ ....   b) $13 < 3x + 1$ ....   c) $3x + 1 < 34$ ....

5. **Explain how your answers to parts b) and c) of question 4 can be used to solve the inequality $13 < 3x + 1 < 34$.**

....

6. **Solve the inequality $3x + 4 < 2x - 5$. Give your answer in the form {x: x < a}, where a is an integer.**

....

Main activity: Using graphs to solve inequalities   Timing: 20 mins

Learning objectives

- Solve inequalities in one or two variables graphically
- Represent the solution set for an inequality using set notation

Equipment

1. $y = x^2 - 2x - 8$

   a) On these axes, draw the graph of this equation.
      Mark all points of intersection with the axes.

   b) Choose the solution set from the box below that matches each of these inequalities.

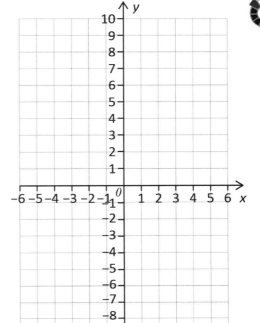

$\{x: -2 \le x \le 4\}$	$\{x: -2 < x < 4\}$
$\{x: x < -2 \text{ or } x > 4\}$	$\{x: x \le -2 \text{ or } x \ge 4\}$
$\{x: -2 < x \le 4\}$	$\{x: -2 \le x < 4\}$
$\{x: x \le -2 \text{ or } x > 4\}$	$\{x: x < -2 \text{ or } x \ge 4\}$

   i) $0 < x^2 - 2x - 8$ ⋯⋯⋯⋯⋯⋯⋯⋯⋯⋯⋯⋯⋯⋯⋯⋯⋯⋯⋯

   ii) $0 \le x^2 - 2x - 8$ ⋯⋯⋯⋯⋯⋯⋯⋯⋯⋯⋯⋯⋯⋯⋯⋯⋯⋯⋯

   iii) $x^2 - 2x - 8 < 0$ ⋯⋯⋯⋯⋯⋯⋯⋯⋯⋯⋯⋯⋯⋯⋯⋯⋯⋯⋯

   iv) $x^2 - 2x - 8 \le 0$ ⋯⋯⋯⋯⋯⋯⋯⋯⋯⋯⋯⋯⋯⋯⋯⋯⋯⋯⋯

2. **On the axes, construct the graphs of $y = -2x + 1$ and $y = -5$.**
   Then write the solution sets for these inequalities:

   a) $x^2 - 2x - 8 > -5$ ⋯⋯⋯⋯⋯⋯⋯⋯⋯⋯⋯⋯⋯⋯⋯⋯⋯⋯⋯⋯⋯⋯

   b) $x^2 - 2x - 8 < -2x + 1$ ⋯⋯⋯⋯⋯⋯⋯⋯⋯⋯⋯⋯⋯⋯⋯⋯⋯⋯⋯⋯

HOMEWORK ACTIVITY: EXAM-STYLE QUESTIONS

TIMING: 25 MINS

LEARNING OBJECTIVES

- Solve linear inequalities in one variable; represent the solution set on a number line

EQUIPMENT

1. *n* is an integer. Given that $-7.5 \leq n < 14.1$, what is the:

   a) smallest value it could be?

   ....
   (1 mark)

   b) largest value it could be?

   ....
   (1 mark)

2. $-3 < 2n - 4 \leq 8$

   a) Solve the inequality.

   ....
   (3 marks)

   b) Represent the solution set on this number line.

   | | | | | | | | | | | | | | | | | | | | | |
   −10 −9 −8 −7 −6 −5 −4 −3 −2 −1 0 1 2 3 4 5 6 7 8 9 10

   (2 marks)

3. Which whole number values of *x* satisfy the inequalities $4x - 5 < 16$ and $-4x + 1 \leq 7$?

   ....
   (3 marks)

4. Solve the inequality $x^2 - 2x < 3$.

   ....
   (3 marks)

14 ANSWERS

STARTER ACTIVITY: ALWAYS, SOMETIMES, NEVER

1.

Always true	Sometimes true	Never true
$a - 5 \leq b - 5$	$\dfrac{a}{4} < \dfrac{b}{4}$	$-a < -b$
	$b + 3 > a + 3$	$5 - b > 10 - a$
	$4a \leq 6b$	
	$a = b$	

MAIN ACTIVITY: INEQUALITIES

1. a) 0, 1, 2, 3, 4   b) −3, −2   c) 1, 2, 3, 4   d) −1, 0, 1, 2, 3

2. a)

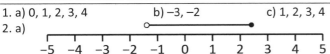

b) $-4 < x \leq 3$

3. a) i) true   ii) true   iii) true   iv) true

b) i) It is no longer true – its orientation switches.   ii) It is no longer true – its orientation switches.

4. a) $x > 7$ b) $4 < x$ c) $x < 11$

5. The two inequalities can be combined to give $4 < x < 11$.

6. $\{x: x < -9\}$

MAIN ACTIVITY: USING GRAPHS TO SOLVE INEQUALITIES

1. a) See graph to right

b) i) $\{x: x < -2 \text{ or } x > 4\}$

ii) $\{x: x \leq -2 \text{ or } x \geq 4\}$

iii) $\{x: -2 < x < 4\}$

iv) $\{x: -2 \leq x \leq 4\}$

2. See graphs to the right.

a) $x^2 - 2x - 8 > -5 \ \{x: x < -1 \text{ or } x > 3\}$

b) $x^2 - 2x - 8 < -2x + 1 \ \{x: -3 < x < 3\}$

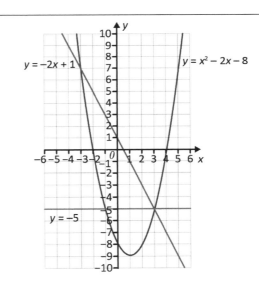

HOMEWORK ACTIVITY: EXAM-STYLE QUESTIONS

1. a) −7   b) 14

2. a) $\dfrac{1}{2} < n \leq 6$ b)

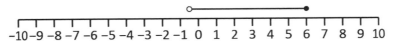

3. − 1, 0, 1, 2, 3, 4, 5

4. $-1 < x < 3$

GLOSSARY

Integer

A whole number; can be positive, negative or zero

MATHS
— HIGHER —

15 ALGEBRA: SEQUENCES

LEARNING OBJECTIVES

- Generate terms of a sequence from a term-to-term or position-to-term rule
- Recognise and use sequences of triangular, square, and cube numbers and simple arithmetic progressions

SPECIFICATION LINKS

- A1, A2, A23, A24, A25

STARTER ACTIVITY

- **Triangular and square numbers; 5 minutes; page 102**
  Ensure that when the student finds the 10th term, they do this by looking at the numerical pattern, e.g. for triangular numbers: 1, 1 + 2, 1 + 2 + 3, … or for square numbers: 1 × 1, 2 × 2, 3 × 3, ….

MAIN ACTIVITIES

- **Terms in a sequence; 20 minutes; page 103**
  Introduce what a sequence is and establish that it can be infinite or finite, ascending or descending. Clarify the definition of 'arithmetic' and 'geometric' sequences. Ask the student to follow the instructions on the activity sheet.
- **Finding the general term; 20 minutes; page 104**
  Model how to find the general term of a linear sequence, then ask the student to complete questions 1 and 2 on the activity sheet. Afterwards, work through the worked example with the student. Discuss how to find the general term of a quadratic sequence before the student moves on to complete question 3.

PLENARY ACTIVITY

- **Types of sequence; 5 minutes**
  Brainstorm all the different types of sequence that the student has encountered in the lesson. Ensure that you include: square, triangular, cube, Fibonacci, arithmetic, geometric, linear and quadratic. Ask the student to give an example of each type of sequence.

HOMEWORK ACTIVITY

- **Sequence problems; 30 minutes; page 105**
  Full instructions are given on the activity sheet.

SUPPORT IDEA

- **Finding the general term** When finding the general term of an arithmetic sequence, encourage the student to write the sequence of the multiples of the common difference underneath the first. This makes it easy to compare their sequence to the sequence of multiples:
  e.g. for the sequence: 2, 5, 8, 11
  compare it to the sequence: 3, 6, 9, 12
  The student should notice that the sequence is 1 less than the multiple of 3: $3n - 1$.
  To find the general term of a quadratic sequence, use the same process but write the terms of the sequence an^2 underneath the sequence (where a = second difference ÷ 2).

EXTENSION IDEA

- **Finding the general term** Rather than showing the student the method for finding the general term of a quadratic sequence, invite the student to generate terms of the sequences n^2, $2n^2$, $3n^2$, … etc. Ask the student to find the second row of differences. Challenge the student to identify how this relates to the coefficient of n^2.

PROGRESS AND OBSERVATIONS

STARTER ACTIVITY: TRIANGULAR AND SQUARE NUMBERS   TIMING: 5 MINS

LEARNING OBJECTIVES

- Recognise and use sequences of triangular, square and cube numbers

EQUIPMENT

1. Look at this pattern. It shows the triangular numbers.

a) Continue the sequence by drawing the next term above.

b) How many dots are there in each of the first six terms of the sequence?

c) Work out how many dots there will be in the 10th term.

2. Look at this pattern. It shows the square numbers.

a) Continue the sequence by drawing the next term.

b) How many dots are there in each of the first six terms of the sequence shown?

c) Work out how many dots there will be in the 10th term.

3. Why do you think these sequences are called the 'square numbers' and 'triangular numbers'?

MAIN ACTIVITY: TERMS IN A SEQUENCE

TIMING: 20 MINS

LEARNING OBJECTIVES

- Generate terms of a sequence from a term-to-term or position-to-term rule
- Recognise and use sequences of triangular, square and cube numbers and simple arithmetic progressions

EQUIPMENT

1. **Generate the first five terms of the sequences with these n^{th} terms.**

   a) $3n + 1$ ....

   b) n^2 ....

   c) $3n^2 - 2n$ ....

   d) $\dfrac{5n}{4}$ ....

   e) $(n + 1)(n - 1)$ ....

2. **Look at the difference between consecutive terms in the sequences in question 1. Explain what you notice about the quadratic and linear sequences.**

   ....

3. **This function machine generates terms in a sequence.**

   input → | −5 | → | ×3 | → output

   To find the next term in the sequence, input the previous term. The first term of the sequence is 7.

   a) Find the 2nd term. ....

   b) How many positive terms will there be in the sequence? ....

4. **Generate the first five terms of the sequences with these n^{th} terms. For each sequence, describe the term-to-term rule to your tutor.**

   a) 3^n ....

   b) $(-1)^n$ ....

   c) $\sqrt{7}^n$ ....

5. **What do you notice about the sequences in question 4? Explain why this is.**

   ....

6. **Which sequences in this activity are geometric and which are arithmetic? Can you identify them from their general term?**

   ....

MAIN ACTIVITY: FINDING THE GENERAL TERM

TIMING: 20 MINS

LEARNING OBJECTIVES

- Deduce expressions to calculate the nth term of a linear, quadratic or geometric sequence

EQUIPMENT

1. **Decide which of these sequences are arithmetic and which are geometric.**

    a) 10, 8, 6, …   ....

    b) −9, −4, 1, …   ....

    c) 10, 5, 2.5, …   ....

    d) 1, 3, 9, 27, …   ....

2. **Find the nth term of each of the arithmetic sequences in question 1.**

Example:

Find the nth term of the sequence: 0, 5, 12, 21, …

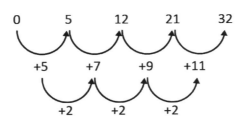

The second row of differences is +2, so the general term is of the form $n^2 + an + b$.
Subtracting n^2 from the original sequence gives: −1, 1, 3, 5, 7, … The general term is $2n − 3$.
Therefore, the general term of the sequence is $n^2 + 2n − 3$.

---

3. **Find the nth term of each of these sequences.**

    Hint: If the 2ⁿᵈ row of differences is not 2, divide by 2 to find the coefficient of a^2. For example, if the 2ⁿᵈ row of differences is 10, then the general term will be of the form $5n^2 + an + b$.

    a) 6, 9, 14, 21, 30, …   ....

    b) 4, 6, 10, 16, 24, …   ....

    c) 0, 11, 28, 51, 80, …   ....

HOMEWORK ACTIVITY: SEQUENCE PROBLEMS

TIMING: 30 MINS

LEARNING OBJECTIVES

- Generate terms of a sequence from a term-to-term or position-to-term rule
- Recognise and use sequences of triangular, square and cube numbers and simple arithmetic progressions
- Deduce expressions to calculate the nth term of a linear sequence

EQUIPMENT

1. **A sequence is generated by adding together three consecutive odd numbers:**

   1st term = 1 + 3 + 5 = 9 2nd term = 3 + 5 + 7 = 15 3rd term = 5 + 7 + 9 = 21

   a) What is the 12th term in the sequence?

   ....

   b) Write an expression for the nth term of the sequence.

   ....

   c) Craig says that 95 cannot be a term in the sequence. Is he correct? Explain your answer.

   ....

2. **The general term of a sequence is $10 - n^2$. How many terms larger than −50 will there be in the sequence?**

   ....

3. **The first two terms of a sequence are: 1, $\frac{1}{2}$, ...**

   Suggest values for the next three terms if the sequence is:

   a) arithmetic   ....

   b) geometric   ....

   c) quadratic   ....

4. **Find the general term of each of these sequences.**

   a) $-\frac{1}{2}, \frac{1}{4}, -\frac{1}{8}, \frac{1}{16}, -\frac{1}{32}, ...$ ....

   b) 4, 13, 28, 49, 76, ...

   c) 1, 8, 27, 64, 125, ...

15 ANSWERS

STARTER ACTIVITY: TRIANGULAR AND SQUARE NUMBERS

1. a)   b) 1, 3, 6, 10, 15   c) 55 dots

2. a)   b) 1, 4, 9, 16, 25, 36   c) 100 dots

3. Student's own answers

MAIN ACTIVITY: TERMS IN A SEQUENCE

1. a) 4, 7, 10, 13, 16   b) 1, 4, 9, 16, 25   c) 1, 8, 21, 40, 65

d) $\frac{5}{4}, \frac{10}{4}, \frac{15}{4}, \frac{20}{4}, \frac{25}{4} = 1\frac{1}{4}, 2\frac{1}{2}, 3\frac{3}{4}, 5, 6\frac{1}{4}$ e) 0, 3, 8, 15, 24

2. Linear sequences increase/decrease by a common difference. In quadratic sequences, the difference increases/decreases by a common difference.

3. a) 6   b) 3

4. a) 3, 9, 27, 81, 243   b) −1, 1, −1, 1, −1   c) $\sqrt{7}, 7, 7\sqrt{7}, 49, 49\sqrt{7}$

5. The term-to-term rule is always multiply by the base because each term is an increasing power of the base.

6. Arithmetic: question 1 a) and d). Geometric: all of question 4.

MAIN ACTIVITY: FINDING THE GENERAL TERM

1. a) and b) are arithmetic; c) and d) are geometric

2. a) $-2n + 12$ b) $5n - 14$

3. a) $n^2 + 5$ b) $n^2 - n + 4$ c) $3n^2 + 2n - 5$

HOMEWORK ACTIVITY: SEQUENCE PROBLEMS

1. a) 23 + 25 + 27 = 75   b) $6n + 3$

c) Craig is correct. Either: $6n + 3 = 95$, $n = 15\frac{1}{3}$, which is not a whole number. Or: All the terms in the sequence are multiples of 3; 95 is not a multiple of 3.

2. 7

3. a) 0, $-\frac{1}{2}$, −1   b) Student's own answer; example: $\frac{1}{4}, \frac{1}{8}, \frac{1}{16}$ c) Student's own answer; example: −2, $-6\frac{1}{2}$, −13

4. a) $\left(-\frac{1}{2}\right)^n$ b) $3n^2 + 1$ c) n^3

GLOSSARY

Arithmetic sequence
A sequence in which the difference between consecutive terms is constant

Geometric sequence
A sequence in which the ratio between consecutive terms is constant

16 ALGEBRA: LINEAR, QUADRATIC, CUBIC AND RECIPROCAL GRAPHS

LEARNING OBJECTIVES

- Use the form $mx + c$ to identify parallel and perpendicular lines
- Find the equation of the line through two given points or through one point given the gradient
- Recognise, sketch and interpret graphs of quadratic, cubic and reciprocal functions

SPECIFICATION LINKS

- A8, A9, A10, A11, A12

STARTER ACTIVITY

- **Match it up!; 5 minutes; page 108**
  Ask the student to match the graphs to their equations ($y = \pm a$, $x = \pm a$, $y = x$ and $y = -x$).

MAIN ACTIVITIES

- **Linear graphs; 15 minutes; page 109**
  Model how to plot a graph in the form $y = mx + c$. Extend to plotting graphs of the form $ax + by = c$.
  Invite the student to recognise the relationship between the gradient and the m value in the equation, encouraging the student to notice that for an increase of 1 in the x-direction, the y-value will increase by 'm'. Discuss the y-intercept and how and why this can be found from the equation of the graph. Ask the student to work through the activity by following the instructions provided.

- **Curves; 25 minutes; page 110**
  Discuss the shape of quadratic functions, cubic functions and reciprocal functions. Sketch the graphs of
  $y = x^2 + 2x - 3$, $y = -x^3 + 2x^2 + 4x - 2$ and $y = \dfrac{1}{x}$ by plotting points. Discuss the properties of these three types of graph.

  Draw out the meaning of the terms roots, intercept, turning point, maximum and minimum.
  Ask the student to work through the activity sheet by following the instructions provided.

PLENARY ACTIVITY

- **Terminology; 5 minutes**
  Test the student on the new vocabulary they have learned in this lesson. Ask them to define some words from the following list: quadratic, cubic, linear, turning point, maximum, minimum, root, reciprocal.

HOMEWORK ACTIVITY

- **Graphs; 30 minutes; page 111**
  Full instructions are given on the activity sheet.

SUPPORT IDEA

- **Curves** You may wish to spend some time looking at the features of the three types of curve that the student is likely to encounter (quadratic, cubic and reciprocal). Identify the points where the curves cross the axes and the maximum/minimum points. You could do this using a graph-sketching package or website.

EXTENSION IDEA

- **Curves** Ask the student to note that the points where graphs cross the x- or y-axes are called intercepts. Where two graphs (lines) cross, they intersect. Challenge the student to decide if a pair of graphs will intercept, and then justify how they know (algebraically or graphically).

PROGRESS AND OBSERVATIONS

STARTER ACTIVITY: MATCH IT UP!

TIMING: **5 MINS**

LEARNING OBJECTIVES

- Plot and recognise the graphs of $y = \pm a$, $x = \pm a$, $y = x$ and $y = -x$

EQUIPMENT

1. Match each equation to the correct graph by writing the appropriate letter next to each equation.

a) $y = 3$ ....

b) $x = 3$ ....

c) $x = -2$ ....

d) $y = 2$ ....

e) $x = 0.5$ ....

f) $y = -3$ ....

g) $y = x$ ....

h) $y = -x$ ....

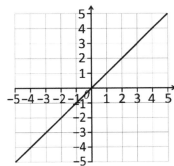

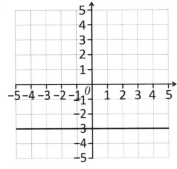

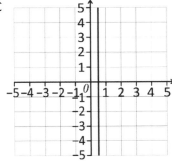

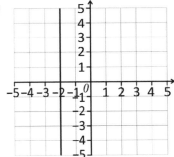

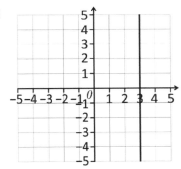

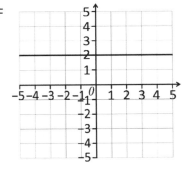

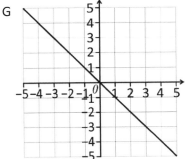

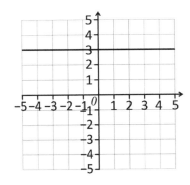

MAIN ACTIVITY: LINEAR GRAPHS   TIMING: 15 MINS

LEARNING OBJECTIVES

- Find the equation of a straight line given two points or one point and the gradient

EQUIPMENT

- ruler

1. Mark any two points on the coordinate axes shown.

Calculate the gradient and use this to find the equation of the line joining the two points.

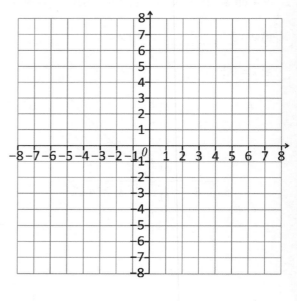

2. Here are the equations of four straight line graphs:

graph A: $y = 3x - 5$ graph B: $6y + 6x = 30$ graph C: $x - y = 10$ graph D: $3x = 3y - 2$

a) Which two graphs are parallel?   --

b) Which two graphs intersect the y-axis at the same point?   --

c) Which two graphs are perpendicular?   --

3. Find the equation of the straight line graph that:

a) has a gradient of 4 and goes through the point (2, −3)

----

b) goes through the points (1, 1) and (4, 7)

----

c) is perpendicular to the line $2y + 6x = 7$ and goes through the origin.

MAIN ACTIVITY: CURVES

TIMING: 25 MINS

LEARNING OBJECTIVES

- Recognise, sketch and interpret graphs of quadratic, cubic and reciprocal functions

EQUIPMENT

- graph paper

1. **Draw lines to match each word to its definition.**

Word		Definition
root		The smallest value that an equation can have for any value of the variable
y-intercept		An equation with the highest power of the variable being 3
turning point		The point where a graph crosses the x-axis, where $y = 0$
minimum		The largest value that an equation can have for any value of the variable
maximum		The point where the graph's gradient is zero; it can be a maximum or minimum point
quadratic equation		An equation with the highest power of the variable being 2
cubic equation		The point where a graph crosses the y-axis, where $x = 0$

2. **This is the graph of $y = x^2 + 2x - 3$.**

    a) What are the coordinates of the points where the graph crosses:

    i) the x-axis .... ii) the y-axis? ....

    b) What are the coordinates of the turning point of the graph?

    ----

    c) What is the equation of the line of symmetry of the graph?

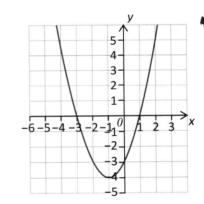

3. **$2x^2 + 8x - 10$**

    a) Write this expression in the form $a(x + b)^2 + c$, where a, b and c are integers.

    ----

    b) Write this expression in the form $(ax + b)(x + c)$, where a, b and c are integers.

    ----

    c) Use the information from parts a) and b) to sketch the graph of $y = 2x^2 + 8x - 10$, marking on the minimum point and the points where the graph crosses the axis.

HOMEWORK ACTIVITY: GRAPHS   TIMING: 30 MINS

LEARNING OBJECTIVES
- Recognise quadratic, cubic, reciprocal and linear graphs
- Find approximate solutions using graphs

EQUIPMENT
- graph paper

 1. **a) Look at the shape of each graph and decide if it is linear, quadratic, cubic or reciprocal.**

i) 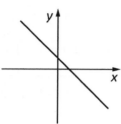   ii) 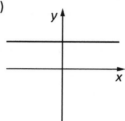   iii) 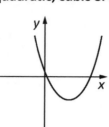   iv)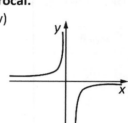

v) 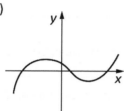   vi) 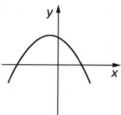   vii) 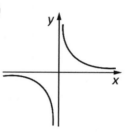   viii)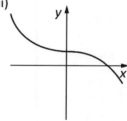

i) ....   ii) ....   iii) ....   iv) ....

v) ....   vi) ....   vii) ....   viii) ....

b) Mark any turning points with a blue cross.

d) Mark any roots with a green cross.

c) Mark any points of intersection with the *y*-axis with a red cross.

e) Draw a dotted line to indicate any lines of symmetry.

 2. **For the graph of $y = 2x^2 + 3x - 5$, find:**

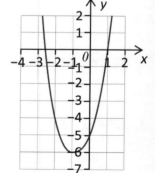

a) the value of *y* when $x = 0$ ....   b) the values of *x* when $y = 0$ ....

c) the smallest possible value of *y*   ....

d) the equation of the line of symmetry   ....

e) Explain why you can't find the largest value of *y*.

....

 3. **On graph paper, sketch the graphs of:**

a) $y = \dfrac{4}{x}$ b) $y = x^3 + 5$ c) $y = 3x^2 + 6x - 9$

4. **On the graphs, mark any turning points where the graph intercepts the axes, and all of the maximum and minimum points.**

16 ANSWERS

STARTER ACTIVITY: MATCH IT UP!

1. a) H   b) E   c) D   d) F   e) C   f) B   g) A   h) G

MAIN ACTIVITY: LINEAR GRAPHS

1. Check the student's answers.
2. a) C and D   b) A and B   c) B and C
3. a) $y = 4x - 11$ b) $y = 2x - 1$ (or equivalent)   c) $3y = x$ (or equivalent)

MAIN ACTIVITY: CURVES

1. **root:** The point where a graph crosses the x-axis, where $y = 0$; **y-intercept:** The point where a graph crosses the y-axis, where $x = 0$; **turning point:** The point where the graph's gradient is zero; it can be a maximum or minimum point; **minimum:** the smallest value that an equation can have for any value of the variable; **maximum:** The largest value that an equation can have for any value of the variable; **quadratic equation:** An equation with the highest power of the variable being 2; **cubic equation:** An equation with the highest power of the variable being 3

2. a) i) $(-3, 0)$ and $(1, 0)$ ii) $(0, -3)$ b) $(-1, -4)$ c) $x = -1$
3. a) $2(x + 2)^2 - 18$ b) $(2x - 2)(x + 5)$
c) Minimum at $(-2, -18)$; crosses x-axis when $x = 1$ and $x = -5$; crosses y-axis at -10

HOMEWORK ACTIVITY: GRAPHS

1. a) i) linear   ii) linear   iii) quadratic   iv) reciprocal
v) cubic   vi) quadratic   vii) reciprocal   viii) cubic
b)–e) Check student's graphs.

2. a) -5 b) 1 or $-2\frac{1}{2}$ c) -6.125 d) $x = -0.75$

e) The value of y will continue to increase as x increases/decreases.

3. a) 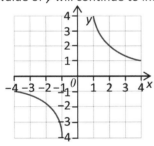   b) 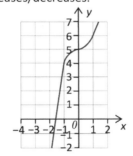   c)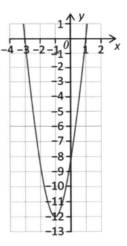

4. a) $y = \dfrac{4}{x}$; no points to mark

b) $y = x^3 + 5$; turning point at $(0, 5)$; crosses y-axis at $(0, 5)$ and x-axis at $\left(\sqrt[3]{-5}, 0\right)$
c) $y = 3x^2 + 6x - 9$; minimum at $(-1, -12)$; crosses x-axis at $(-3, 0)$ and $(1, 0)$ and

y-axis at $(0, -9)$

GLOSSARY

Gradient
The steepness of a line, measured as change in y for change of 1 in x

Turning point
A point at which the gradient of a graph is zero

Root
The value when a function is equal to zero

Maximum
A point at which the gradient of a graph changes from positive to negative

Minimum
A point at which the gradient of a graph changes from negative to positive

17 ALGEBRA: INTERPRETING GRAPHS

LEARNING OBJECTIVES

- Draw and interpret distance–time graphs
- Identify and interpret roots, intercepts, turning points, area under and gradient of graphs, relating them to real-life problems

SPECIFICATION LINKS

- A10, A11, A12, A14, A15

STARTER ACTIVITY

- **Filling vases; 5 minutes; page 114**
  Explain that water is poured into each vase at a steady rate. Ask the student to match each graph showing height of water against time with the correctly shaped vase. Discuss with the student how the gradient of the graph changes over time for each vase.

MAIN ACTIVITIES

- **Interpreting graphs; 30 minutes; page 115**
  Remind the student how to sketch a linear graph using the y-intercept and gradient. Make sure the student understands that gradient means rate of change. Look again at the graphs of the vases filling in the starter activity and discuss how the gradients changed over time and how to identify when each vase was filling fastest.
  Look at the graph on the activity sheet and explain that the axes are not labelled; they will consider three scenarios. For each scenario, establish the meaning of the x and y intercepts, the gradient (if appropriate), the area under the graph (if appropriate), and the meaning of the 'stationary point'. Calculate an estimate for the gradient using a tangent at a fixed point for each scenario, and discuss what this means. For scenario 3, estimate the area under the graph using trapeziums.
- **Distance–time and speed–time graphs; 10 minutes; page 116**
  Full instructions are given on the activity sheet.

PLENARY ACTIVITY

- **Finding the area under a curve; 5 minutes**
  Discuss how to find an estimate for the area under a curve. You may wish to look at ways in which this could be done using the graph on *Interpreting graphs*. Establish that you could use rectangles/triangles/trapeziums, and discuss which would give the most accurate answer.

HOMEWORK ACTIVITY

- **All types of graph; 60 minutes; page 117**
  Full instructions are given on the activity sheet.

SUPPORT IDEA

- **Distance–time and speed–time graphs** Simplify the problem by drawing distance–time and speed–time graphs that are linear. Discuss what the gradient shows in each. Extend to what a horizontal line would mean on each type of graph.

EXTENSION IDEA

- **Distance–time and speed–time graphs** Investigate different ways of finding the area under a curve – this might lead to the development of the trapezium rule!

PROGRESS AND OBSERVATIONS

MATHS

— HIGHER —

Edexcel

STARTER ACTIVITY: FILLING VASES

TIMING: 5 MINS

LEARNING OBJECTIVES

- Relate the gradient of graphs to real-life problems

EQUIPMENT

Five different vases are filled with water at a steady rate. The graphs show the height of water in each vase over time. Discuss with your tutor which graph matches which vase. Make sure you can explain how you know.

1.

A.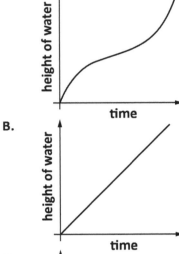

2.

3.

B.

C.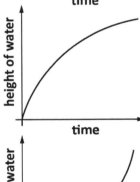

4.

5.

D.

E.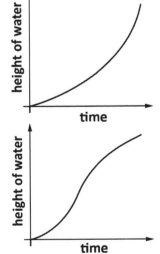

MAIN ACTIVITY: INTERPRETING GRAPHS   TIMING: **30** MINS

LEARNING OBJECTIVES
- Identify and interpret roots, intercepts, turning points, area under and gradient of graphs, relating them to real-life problems

EQUIPMENT
none

1. The axes on the graph below are not labelled. Consider these three scenarios:

- Scenario 1: The *x*-axis shows time in seconds and the *y*-axis shows displacement in kilometres.
- Scenario 2: The *x*-axis shows time in years and the *y*-axis shows population in hundreds of thousands.
- Scenario 3: The *x*-axis shows time in seconds and the *y*-axis shows speed in metres per second.

a) What would the gradient of a tangent at a fixed point represent in each scenario?

----

b) What would the gradient a chord joining two points on the graph represent in each scenario?

----

c) In Scenario 3, what would the area under the graph represent?

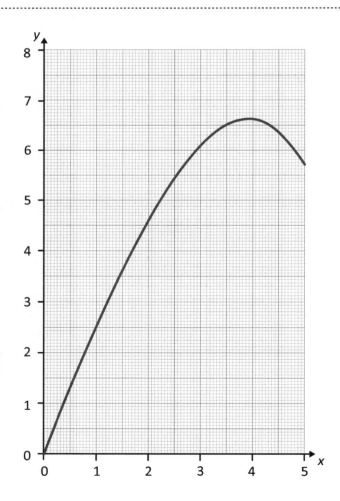

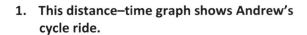
MAIN ACTIVITY: DISTANCE–TIME AND SPEED–TIME GRAPHS TIMING: 10 MINS

LEARNING OBJECTIVES

- Draw and interpret distance–time graphs and speed–time graphs

EQUIPMENT

- plain paper

Write your answers to these questions on a separate sheet of paper.

1. **This distance–time graph shows Andrew's cycle ride.**

   a) How far does Andrew cycle in the first 40 minutes?

   b) Work out his speed in miles per hour during the first 40 minutes of his ride.

   c) What happens between 40 and 60 minutes into his ride? Explain how you know.

   d) When is Andrew cycling fastest? Explain how you know and work out his speed.

   e) How far did Andrew cycle altogether?

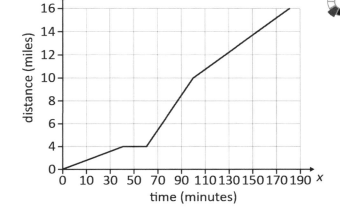

   f) Work out Andrew's average speed for his ride.

2. **Complete the sentences for a distance–time graph.**

   To calculate speed, find the _____ of the graph. A horizontal line indicates that _____

   _____ .

3. **This graph shows the speed, in metres per second, of a ball, *t* seconds after it has been thrown upwards.**

   a) Write the speed of the ball 0.8 s after it has been thrown.

   b) What was the lowest speed of the ball?

   c) When was the ball travelling at 3 m/s?

   d) Calculate the acceleration of the ball at 0.5 s.

   e) Calculate the average acceleration of the ball between 0 and 1 seconds.

   f) Work out the approximate total distance the ball travelled in the first second.

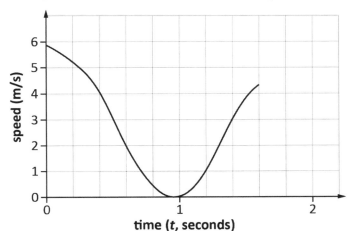

4. **Complete these sentences for a speed–time graph.**

   To calculate acceleration, find the _____ of the graph. To calculate total distance travelled, find the

   _____ the graph. A horizontal line indicates that _____ .

Homework activity: All types of graphs

Timing: 60 mins

Learning objectives

- Know and use the properties of linear graphs, quadratic graphs, cubic graphs reciprocal graphs, distance–time graph and speed–time graphs

Equipment

- plain paper

1. **Produce a set of revision cards or a spider diagram that includes all the facts you have learned about graphs.**

Linear graphs

Include:
- How to find the gradient and y-intercept from the equation
- How to find the equation of a line from two points, and one point and the gradient
- How to identify whether two lines are parallel from their equation
- How to identify whether two lines are perpendicular from their equation
- How to find the equation of a line from the graph

Quadratic graphs

Include:
- How to find the points of intersection with the axis
- How to find the maximum and the minimum
- A sketch of the shape

Cubic graphs

Include:
- How to find points of intersection with axis
- A sketch of the shape

Reciprocal graphs

Include:
- How to find points of intersection with axis
- A sketch of the shape

Distance–time graphs

Include:
- The meaning of the gradient
- The meaning of a stationary point or a horizontal part of the curve

Speed–time graphs

Include:
- The meaning of the gradient
- The meaning of the area under the graph
- The meaning of a stationary point or a horizontal part of the curve.

17 ANSWERS

STARTER ACTIVITY: FILLING VASES

1. B   2. C   3. A   4. D   5. E

MAIN ACTIVITY: INTERPRETING GRAPHS

1. a)–c) Scenario 1: Gradient of graph at a point is the speed; gradient joining two points using a chord is the average speed; maximum point is point where displacement from starting point is largest; change in gradient from positive to negative shows that the displacement changes from increasing to decreasing

Scenario 2: Gradient of graph at a point is the rate of change of population; gradient joining two points using a chord is the average rate of change of population; maximum point is point where the population stops increasing; change in gradient from positive to negative shows that the population starts to decrease

Scenario 3: Gradient of graph at a point is the acceleration; gradient joining two points using a chord is the average acceleration; the area under the graph represents the distance travelled; maximum point is point where acceleration is zero; change in gradient from positive to negative shows that the acceleration changes from positive (speeding up) to negative (slowing down)

MAIN ACTIVITY: DISTANCE–TIME AND SPEED–TIME GRAPHS

1. a) 4 miles   b) 12 mph   c) He has a rest – the line is horizontal.

d) Between 30 and 50 minutes, the gradient is highest, at 18 mph   e) 16 miles   f) $10\frac{2}{3}$ mph

2. a) gradient; the person/vehicle is stationary
3. a) 0.5 m/s   b) 0 m/s   c) 0.5 and 1.4 seconds   d) 10 m/s^2 e) −6 m/s^2
f) 2.8 m
4. a) gradient; area under; speed is constant

HOMEWORK ACTIVITY: ALL TYPES OF GRAPH

1. Check the student's work.

18 ALGEBRA: TRIGONOMETRIC GRAPHS AND TRANSFORMATIONS

LEARNING OBJECTIVES

- Recognise, sketch and interpret graphs of trigonometric functions
- Sketch translations and reflections of a given function

SPECIFICATION LINKS

- A12, A13

STARTER ACTIVITY

- **Shapes of graphs; 5 minutes; page 120**
  Full instructions are given on the activity sheet.

MAIN ACTIVITIES

- **Trigonometric functions; 15 mins; page 121**
  Explain to the student that the worksheet shows all three trigonometric functions. Students must identify each graph. Draw the student's attention to the values of tan x which cannot be calculated (where they tend to infinity). Ask the student to use the graphs to find values of sin x, cos x and tan x. Similarly, ask the student to find approximate values of x given values of sin x, cos x and tan x. Draw the student's attention to the fact that $-1 \leq \sin x \leq 1$ and $-1 \leq \cos x \leq 1$.
- **Transformations of functions; 25 minutes; page 122**
  To support question 1, ask the student to sketch the graphs of $y = x^2 + 2$. Model each transformation by choosing values for 'a' and sketching the transformation with the student. Discuss how each transformation changes the graph. Move on to question 2, discussing the effects that each transformation will have on particular points.

PLENARY ACTIVITY

- **How has it been transformed?; 5 minutes**
  Sketch the graph of $y = x^2$, then sketch a transformation of $y = x^2$. Challenge the student to write down the equation of the transformed graph. Repeat for different transformations. Draw attention to the fact that $y = x^2$ and $y = (-x)^2$ are equivalent since the graph of $y = x^2$ is symmetrical about the y-axis.

HOMEWORK ACTIVITY

- **Vlogging; 60 minutes; page 123**
  Full instructions are given on the activity sheet.

SUPPORT IDEA

- **Transformations of functions** Provide support for question 1 by considering the effect numerically, e.g. draw up a table of values for $y = x^2 + 2$, then compare this to the values for $y = 2(x^2 + 2)$. Which values are altered? How are they altered?

EXTENSION IDEA

- **Transformations of functions** Ask the student to sketch transformations of the trigonometric functions, e.g. $y = \sin x + 1$ or $y = -\cos x$, marking on points of intersection with the axes and maximum and minimum points.

PROGRESS AND OBSERVATIONS

STARTER ACTIVITY: SHAPES OF GRAPHS   TIMING: 5 MINS

LEARNING OBJECTIVES

- Recognise and interpret linear, quadratic, cubic and reciprocal graphs

EQUIPMENT

1. **Draw lines to match the equation of each graph to its diagram. Explain to your tutor how you know which goes with which.**

A: $x = 5$

1.
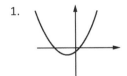

2.
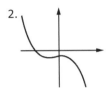

B: $y = 2x - 3$

3.
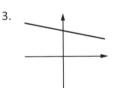

C: $y = -\frac{1}{2}x + 5$

4.
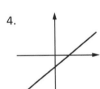

D: $y = x^2 + 2x - 1$

5.
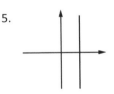

E: $y = -x^2$

6.
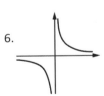

F: $y = -2x^3 - 3x^2 + 2x - 12$

7.

G: $y = 3^x$

8.
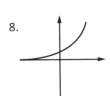

H: $y = \frac{1}{x}$

MAIN ACTIVITY: TRIGONOMETRIC FUNCTIONS

TIMING: 15 MINS

LEARNING OBJECTIVES

- Recognise, sketch and interpret graphs of the trigonometric functions $y = \sin x$, $y = \cos x$ and $y = \tan x$

EQUIPMENT

 1. **These graphs show the three different trigonometric functions. Identify each graph and find the values your tutor asks for.**

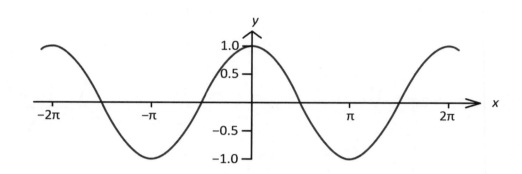

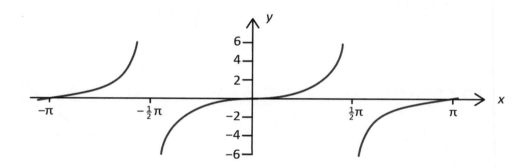

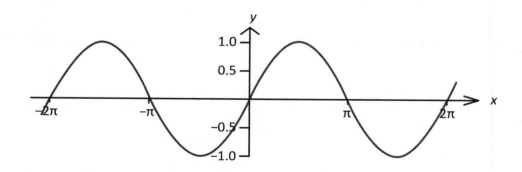

MAIN ACTIVITY: TRANSFORMATIONS OF FUNCTIONS

TIMING: 25 MINS

LEARNING OBJECTIVES

- Recognise, sketch and interpret translations and reflections of a given function

EQUIPMENT

1. **Explain how each of these transformations changes the graph of $y = f(x)$.**

   a) $y = f(x) + a$ ....

   b) $y = f(x + a)$ ....

   c) $y = f(x) - a$ ....

   d) $y = f(x - a)$ ....

   e) $y = f(-x)$ ....

   f) $y = -f(x)$ ....

   g) $y = af(x)$ ....

   h) $y = f(ax)$ ....

2. **This graph shows $y = f(x)$.**

   a) Sketch these graphs on the axes.

      i) $y = f(x + 5)$
      ii) $y = 3f(x)$
      iii) $y = f(-x)$
      iv) $y = f(x) - 7$

   b) Mark the coordinates of the new points of A, B and C.

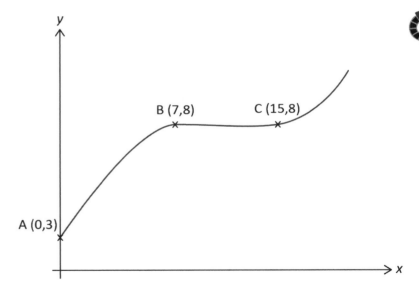

122

HOMEWORK ACTIVITY: VLOGGING

TIMING: 60 MINS

LEARNING OBJECTIVES

- Recognise, sketch and interpret graphs of trigonometric functions
- Sketch translations and reflections of a given function

EQUIPMENT

- video recording equipment such as a smartphone (if available)

1. **Create a vlog (video blog) about transformations of graphs. You could simply write the script if you'd prefer. Sketch some graphs to illustrate your vlog or script. If you want to challenge yourself, try using the trigonometric functions as examples!**

   Make sure you include all of these transformations:

   - $y = f(x) + a$: translation through $\begin{pmatrix} 0 \\ a \end{pmatrix}$

   - $y = f(x + a) - a$: translation through $\begin{pmatrix} -a \\ 0 \end{pmatrix}$

   - $y = f(x) - a$: translation through $\begin{pmatrix} 0 \\ -a \end{pmatrix}$

   - $y = f(x - a) + a$: translation through $\begin{pmatrix} a \\ 0 \end{pmatrix}$

   - $y = f(-x)$: reflected in the y-axis

   - $y = -f(x)$: reflected in the x-axis

   - $y = af(x)$: stretched parallel to the y-axis with scale factor a

   - $y = f(ax)$: stretched parallel to the x-axis with scale factor $\dfrac{1}{a}$

18 ANSWERS

STARTER ACTIVITY: SHAPES OF GRAPHS

1: D   2: F   3: C   4: B   5: A   6: H   7: E   8: G

MAIN ACTIVITY: TRIGONOMETRIC FUNCTIONS

1. The first graph is cos x, the second graph is tan x, the third graph is sin x. Other answers will depend on the questions asked.

MAIN ACTIVITY: TRANSFORMATIONS OF FUNCTIONS

1. a) $y = f(x) + a$ is a translation through $\begin{pmatrix} 0 \\ a \end{pmatrix}$

b) $y = f(x + a)$ is a translation through $\begin{pmatrix} -a \\ 0 \end{pmatrix}$

c) $y = f(x) - a$ is a translation through $\begin{pmatrix} 0 \\ -a \end{pmatrix}$

d) $y = f(x - a)$ is a translation through $\begin{pmatrix} a \\ 0 \end{pmatrix}$

e) $y = f(-x)$ is a reflection in the y-axis

f) $y = -f(x)$ is a reflection in the x-axis

g) $y = af(x)$ is a stretch parallel to the y-axis with scale factor a

h) $y = f(ax)$ is a stretch parallel to the x-axis with scale factor $\dfrac{1}{a}$

2. i)

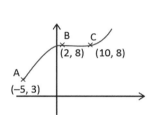

ii)

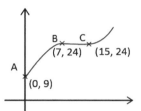

iii)

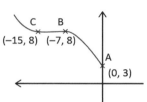

iv)

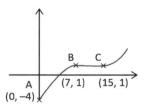

HOMEWORK ACTIVITY: VLOGGING

1. Check the student's vlog and graph sketches.

19 Algebra: Graphs of circles

Learning Objectives

- Recognise and use the equation of a circle
- Find the equation of a tangent to a circle at a given point

Specification Links

- N8, A8, A9, A11, A12, A16

Starter Activity

- **Simplifying surds; 5 minutes; page 126**

  Explain to the student that because the area of a circle is $A = \pi r^2$, the radius can be found by calculating $\sqrt{\dfrac{A}{\pi}}$, which is a surd. This activity will give some practice with this to help make such calculations easier.

Main Activities

- **Sketching graphs; 20 minutes; page 127**
  Remind the student of the equation of a circle and link this to the example given.
  Ask the student to follow the instructions on the activity sheet.
- **Problem solving with circles; 20 minutes; page 128**
  Discuss the relationship between the radius of a circle and a tangent (they are perpendicular), and explain that you might need to use this fact to help you solve problems involving circles. Revise how to find the length of a line segment, the gradient of a line segment, the gradient of a perpendicular line, and the equation of a line given the gradient and a point. Ask the student to follow the instructions on the activity sheet.

Plenary Activity

- **What equation?; 5 minutes**
  Challenge the student to give you the equation of a circle, a quadratic or a linear graph, given particular information.
  For example, a circle with its centre at the origin, radius 6; a quadratic equation that crosses the x-axis at the points 1 and 2; a straight line that crosses the y-axis at 7.

Homework Activity

- **Equations of graphs; 30 minutes; page 129**
  Full instructions are given on the activity sheet.

Support Idea

- **Problem solving with circles** Spend some time sketching circles with different radii and finding the gradient of the different radii before moving on to this activity.

Extension Idea

- **Sketching graphs** Investigate how to transform circles, e.g. plot the graph of $(x + 2)^2 + y^2 = 25$. Link this to transformations of graphs.

Progress and Observations

MATHS
— HIGHER —

Edexcel

STARTER ACTIVITY: SIMPLIFYING SURDS

TIMING: 5 MINS

LEARNING OBJECTIVES

- Simplify surd expressions

EQUIPMENT

1. **Write each of these as a multiple of** $\sqrt{3}$ **. Then write them in ascending order.**

$2\sqrt{3} + 7\sqrt{3}$ 　　　　 $\sqrt{75}$ 　　　　 $\sqrt{27}$ 　　　　 $\dfrac{1}{\sqrt{3}}$ 　　　　 $\dfrac{\sqrt{6}}{\sqrt{2}}$

....　　 ....　　 ....　　 ....　　 ....

....　　 ....　　 ....　　 ....　　 ....

MATHS
— HIGHER —

Edexcel

MAIN ACTIVITY: SKETCHING GRAPHS

TIMING: 20 MINS

LEARNING OBJECTIVES

- Recognise and use the equation of a circle

EQUIPMENT

The equation of a circle with its centre at the origin is $x^2 + y^2 = r^2$, where r = radius of the circle.

For example, this circle has the equation $x^2 + y^2 = 25$.

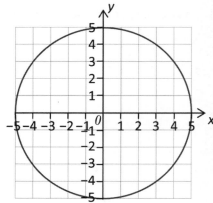

1. **Decide whether each equation is quadratic, linear, or a circle. Rearrange it if necessary and then sketch it on the axes provided.**

a) $2x^2 + 2y = 6$

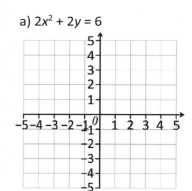

b) $x + y = 3$

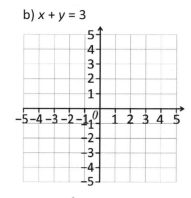

c) $y^2 = 9 - x^2$

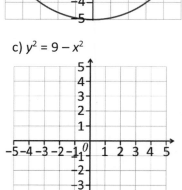

d) $2y^2 + 2x^2 = 8$

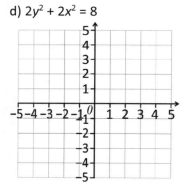

e) $y = 6x^2$

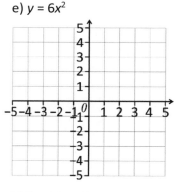

f) $y - x = 1$

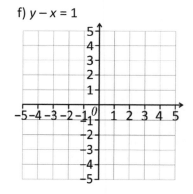

g) $y^2 - 1 = -x^2$

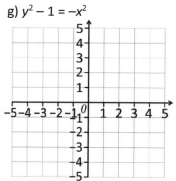

h) $3y - 6x = 9$

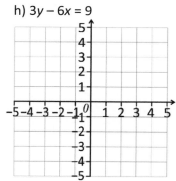

MAIN ACTIVITY: PROBLEM SOLVING WITH CIRCLES

TIMING: 20 MINS

LEARNING OBJECTIVES

- Recognise and use the equation of a circle
- Find the equation of a tangent to a circle at a given point

EQUIPMENT

1. A circle has the equation $x^2 + y^2 = 20$.

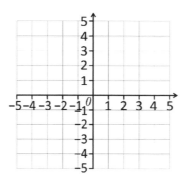

a) Sketch the circle on the axes.

b) Where is O, the centre of the circle? ....

c) What is the radius of the circle? Simplify your answer. ....

d) Show that point A (2, 4) lies on the circle. ....

e) Draw a line joining O with A. Call this l_1. ....

f) Work out the gradient of the line joining O with A. ....

g) Work out an equation of the line OA. ....

h) Draw a tangent to the circle at the point A. Call this line l_2. ....

i) Write the gradient of l_2. ....

j) Work out an equation for line l_2. ....

k) l_2 crosses the x-axis at point B. Work out the coordinates of point B. ....

l) Calculate the area of triangle OAB. ....

HOMEWORK ACTIVITY: EQUATIONS OF GRAPHS   TIMING: 30 MINS

LEARNING OBJECTIVES
- Recognise and use the equation of a circle
- Find the equation of a tangent to a circle at a given point
- Find the equation of linear and quadratic graphs

EQUIPMENT
none

1. **Find the equation of each of the following graphs:**

    a) The straight line that goes through the points (−1, 4) and (3, 12)

    b) The straight line that is parallel to the graph $y = 3x − 2$, which cuts the x-axis at the point (0, −4)

    c) The straight line that is perpendicular to the graph $y = -\frac{1}{2}x + 5$, which goes through the point (3, 5)

    d) The equation of a curve, which crosses the x-axis at the points (3, 0) and (−5, 0)

    e) The equation of a circle with radius 6

    f) The equation of the perpendicular bisector of the line joining the points (0, 0) and (8, 8)

    g) The equation of the tangent to the circle $x^2 + y^2 = 17$ at the point (−4, −1)

19 ANSWERS

STARTER ACTIVITY: SIMPLIFYING SURDS

1. $\dfrac{1}{\sqrt{3}} = \dfrac{\sqrt{3}}{3}$ $\dfrac{\sqrt{6}}{\sqrt{2}} = \sqrt{3}$ $\sqrt{27} = 3\sqrt{3}$ $\sqrt{75} = 5\sqrt{3}$ $2\sqrt{3} + 7\sqrt{3} = 9\sqrt{3}$

MAIN ACTIVITY: SKETCHING GRAPHS

1. a) 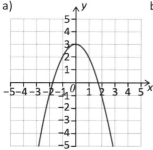   b) 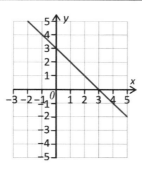   c) 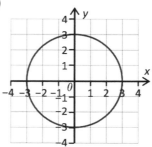   d)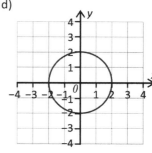

e) 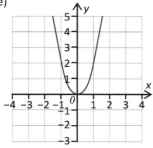   f) 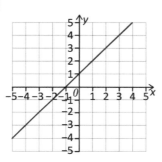   g) 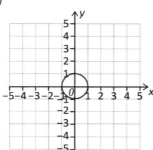   h)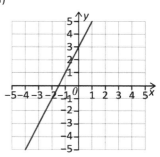

MAIN ACTIVITY: PROBLEM SOLVING WITH CIRCLES

1. a)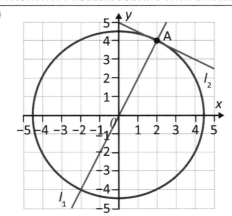

b) (0, 0)   c) $2\sqrt{5}$ d) 22 + 42 = 4 + 16 = 20

e) See graph   f) 2

g) $y = 2x$ h) see graph   i) $-\dfrac{1}{2}$ j) $y = -\dfrac{1}{2} + 5$

k) (10, 0)   l) 20 units^2

HOMEWORK ACTIVITY: EQUATIONS OF GRAPHS

1. a) $y = 2x + 6$ b) $y = 3x - 4$ c) $y = 2x - 1$ d) $y = m(x - 3)(x + 5)$
e) $x^2 + y^2 = 36$ f) $y = -x + 8$ g) $y = -4x - 17$

20 RATIO, PROPORTION AND RATES OF CHANGE: RATIO

LEARNING OBJECTIVES

- Use ratio notation including reduction to its simplest form
- Divide a quantity into a ratio
- Express a multiplicative relationship as a ratio or fraction

SPECIFICATION LINKS

- R4, R5, R6, R7, R8

STARTER ACTIVITY

- **Matching graphs; 5 minutes; page 132**
  Full instructions are given on the activity sheet.

MAIN ACTIVITIES

- **Bags of sweets; 20 minutes; page 133**
  Introduce ratios and how they show the relationship between two or more quantities. Link ratios to proportion and percentages, and discuss how they can be represented as a linear function.
- **Working with ratios; 20 minutes; page 134**
  Establish how to cancel down a ratio and how to share in a given ratio before asking the student to complete the activity sheet.

PLENARY ACTIVITY

- **Recipe ratio; 5 minutes**
  Write a simple recipe for something with only a few ingredients e.g. meringues, a cake or a smoothie – choose your own or source one online. Ask questions based around the recipe, e.g. What is the ratio of flour to sugar? What fraction of the recipe is flour?

HOMEWORK ACTIVITY

- **Practising your ratio skills; 30 minutes; page 135**
  Full instructions are given on the activity sheet.

SUPPORT IDEA

- **Bags of sweets** Use the bar model to support the student's understanding of ratio. For example, if you have a ratio of 2 : 3, represent this as shown. When sharing in a given ratio, each 'box' must contain the same amount. This method makes it clear that the total amount is divided by the sum of the two sides of the ratio.

the whole

2 parts   3 parts

EXTENSION IDEA

- **Bags of sweets** Challenge the student to write a problem for you to solve. The student must include enough information for the problem to have a unique answer.

PROGRESS AND OBSERVATIONS

MATHS
— HIGHER —

STARTER ACTIVITY: MATCHING GRAPHS

TIMING: 5 MINS

LEARNING OBJECTIVES

• Relate ratios to linear functions

EQUIPMENT

1. **Match each description of the relationship between the *x* and *y* values with one of the four graphs below.**

a) The *y* values are twice the *x* values. ....

b) The *x* values are half of the *y* values. ....

c) Each *x* value is a third of the *y* value. ....

d) The *y* values are three times the *x* values. ....

e) *x* is three times larger than *y*. ....

f) The *y* values are a third of the *x* values. ....

g) The *y* values are half of the *x* values. ....

h) Each *x* value is twice the *y* value. ....

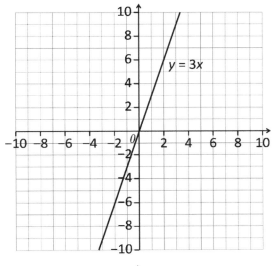

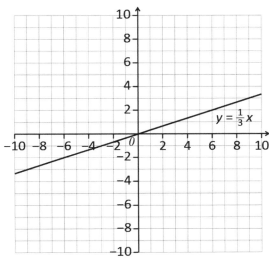

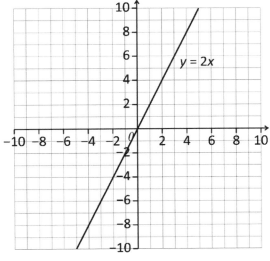

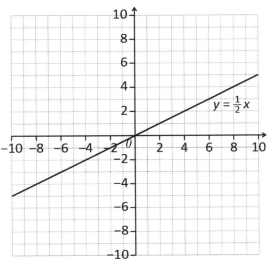

MAIN ACTIVITY: BAGS OF SWEETS

TIMING: 20 MINS

LEARNING OBJECTIVES	EQUIPMENT
• Use ratio notation and reduce a ratio to its simplest form • Divide a quantity into a ratio • Relate ratios to fractions or linear functions	none

1. **Some facts about bags of sweets are given in the table below. Use these facts to complete the final column in the table.**

Bag	Number of sweets	Clues	Number of sweets of each colour
A	24	There are only red and green sweets. The ratio of red to green sweets is 1 : 5.	red: green:
B	30	The bag contains red, yellow and green sweets. The ratio of red to yellow to green sweets is 1 : 2 : 3.	red: yellow: green:
C	15	The bag contains red, green and yellow sweets. The ratio of green to yellow is 1 : 2. There is 1 less red sweet than there are green sweets.	red: green: yellow:
D	34	The bag contains green, red and orange sweets. The ratio of red to orange is 2 : 5. The ratio of green to orange is 3 : 10.	green: red: orange:
E	25	The bag contains blue, pink and yellow sweets. There are twice as many pink sweets as blue sweets, and five more yellow sweets than blue sweets.	blue: pink: yellow:

2. **Use the table to answer these questions.**

   a) What proportion of bag E is blue? ....

   b) What proportion of bag C is green or yellow? ....

   c) What percentage of bag E is pink? ....

   d) Write the ratio of red to orange to green sweets in bag D in the ratio $1 : m : n$.

   ....

MAIN ACTIVITY: WORKING WITH RATIOS   **TIMING: 20 MINS**

LEARNING OBJECTIVES

- Divide a quantity into a ratio
- Express a multiplicative relationship as a ratio or fraction

EQUIPMENT

1. Simplify these ratios.

a) 50 ml : 2 litre   ....

b) 0.5 : 1.2   ....

c) 3.5 m : 70 cm   ....

d) $\frac{1}{2} : \frac{1}{4}$ ....

e) 3 hours : 1 hour 30 minutes   ....

f) 3.9 : 8.1   ....

2. Annika and Boris share £240 in the ratio 1 : 5.
How much more than Annika does Boris get?   ....

3. In a recipe, the weight of sugar to flour is in the ratio 2 : 3.
If there is 50 g more flour than sugar, how much sugar is used?   ....

4. In a box of chocolates, the ratio of milk to dark to white chocolate is 2 : 3 : 5.

a) What fraction of the chocolates is white chocolate?   ....

b) There are 30 chocolates in the box. How many are there of each type?   ....

5. To make pink paint, a factory mixes white and red paint in the ratio 3 : 5. If they use 150 ml of white paint:

a) How much red paint do they use?   ....

b) How much pink paint do they make? Give your answer in litres.   ....

6. In a school, there are 250 students of which 160 are boys. In 1R there are 22 boys and 15 girls. Is the proportion of boys and girls in the school the same as in class 1R? Explain your answer.

....

7. In a litter of puppies, two puppies are brown. The rest are white. The ratio of brown to white puppies is 1 : 3.

a) What fraction of puppies is brown? ....   b) How many puppies are white? ....

c) Write an equation that links the number of brown puppies (*b*) to the number of white puppies (*w*).

....

8. In a recipe, oil and vinegar are mixed in the ratio $\frac{1}{2} : 1\frac{3}{4}$.

Write this ratio in the form 1 : *m* and use this to work out the volume of oil required to make 270 ml of the mixture.   ....

HOMEWORK ACTIVITY: PRACTISING YOUR RATIO SKILLS   TIMING: 30 MINS

LEARNING OBJECTIVES
- Divide a quantity into a ratio
- Express a multiplicative relationship as a ratio or fraction
- Relate ratios to fractions or linear functions
- Solve problems involving ratio

EQUIPMENT
- red, orange and green coloured pencils

Each question will test you on a different skill involving ratios. Colour the traffic light to show how confident you are with each question: green if you are confident, orange if you are nearly there, and red if you found it tricky.

1. **Sharing in a given ratio**

   a) Two friends share £150 in the ratio 2 : 3. Work out how much they each receive. ....

   b) A triangle has a perimeter of 200 cm. The sides are in the ratio 4 : 5 : 7. What is the length of the longest side?   ....

   c) To bake a cake, Ruby mixes flour, sugar and butter in the ratio 3 : 2 : 1. She mixes 300 g of cake mix. How much sugar does she use?   ....

2. **Writing ratios as fractions**

   a) Two friends share a bag of sweets in the ratio 5 : 1. Amy gets more. What fraction does she have?   ....

   b) 50 ml of lavender oil, 10 ml of rose oil and 25 ml of water are mixed to make a perfume.

      i)   Write and simplify the ratio of lavender oil to rose oil to water.   ....

      ii) What fraction of the perfume is water?   ....

3. **Writing ratios as linear functions**

   a) The ratio of blue-eyed children to brown-eyed children is 3 : 1. Write an equation that links the number of blue-eyed children (B) to the number of brown-eyed children (E).   ....

   b) The ratio of red to green paint in a tin is 0.2 : 0.7. Write an equation linking the volume of red paint (r) to the volume of green paint (g).   ....

4. **Solving problems involving ratios**

   a) Amie, Brian and Ruth share the royalties on a book in the ratio 3 : 5 : 7. Given that Ruth receives £800 more than Amie, what is the total amount of royalties received by all three?   ....

   b) A picture has width $5\frac{1}{4}$ inches, height $2\frac{1}{2}$ inches. The ratio of width to height can be expressed in the form 1 : m. What is the value of m?   ....

20 ANSWERS

STARTER ACTIVITY: MATCHING GRAPHS

1. a) $y = 2x$ b) $y = 2x$ c) $y = 3x$ d) $y = 3x$

e) $y = \frac{1}{3}x$ f) $y = \frac{1}{3}x$ g) $y = \frac{1}{2}x$ h) $y = \frac{1}{2}x$

MAIN ACTIVITY: BAGS OF SWEETS

1.

Bag	Number of sweets of each colour
A	4 red, 20 green
B	5 red, 10 yellow, 15 green
C	3 red, 4 green, 8 yellow
D	6 green, 8 red, 20 orange
E	5 blue, 10 pink and 10 yellow

2. a) $\frac{1}{5}$ b) $\frac{4}{5}$ c) 40%   d) 1 : 2.5 : 0.75

MAIN ACTIVITY: WORKING WITH RATIOS

1. a) 1 : 40   b) 5 : 12   c) 5 : 1   d) 2 : 1   e) 2 : 1   f) 13 : 27

2. £160

3. 100 g

4. a) $\frac{1}{2}$ b) 6 milk, 9 dark, 15 white

5. a) 250 ml   b) 0.4 litres

6. No – the proportion of boys to girls in the school is 16 : 9; the proportion of boys to girls in 1R is 22 : 15. Since the ratios are not equivalent, the proportions are not equal.

7. a) $\frac{1}{4}$ b) 6   c) $w = 3b$

8. $1 : 3\frac{1}{2}$; 60 ml

HOMEWORK ACTIVITY: PRACTISING YOUR RATIO SKILLS

1. a) £60 and £90   b) 87.5 cm   c) 100 g

2. a) $\frac{5}{6}$ b) i) 10 : 2 : 5   ii) $\frac{5}{17}$

3. a) $B = 3E$ b) $r = 3.5g$

4. a) £3000   b) $\frac{10}{21}$

21 RATIO, PROPORTION AND RATES OF CHANGE: BEARINGS AND SCALE

LEARNING OBJECTIVES

- Measure line segments and angles in geometric figures
- Interpret maps and scale drawings
- Use bearings

SPECIFICATION LINKS

- G1, G2, G15, R2

STARTER ACTIVITY

- **Gingerbread men; 5 minutes; page 138**
  To remind the student about ratios and scale, ask them to answer the recipe questions on the activity. Explain that scales on a map use ratios to show the relationship between the measured distance on the map and the actual distance, in the same way that the recipe ratios show the relationship between different ingredients.

MAIN ACTIVITIES

- **Bearings and scale; 25 minutes; page 139**
  Model how to measure a bearing and remind the student that a bearing is always three digits. Ask the student to measure the bearing of A–E from the central point, marked X. Discuss scale, and ask the student to calculate the distance between X and the points A–E in kilometres. Ask the student to mark points F and G, giving them the bearings and distance (in kilometres) from any point on the diagram. Differentiate according to ability. Ensure that you discuss the fact that distances must be given in sensible units. For example, we would never give a distance of 100 000 cm; it would be converted to 1 km. Challenge the student to work out the distances between pairs of points if the scale is different. You could use these scales: a) 1 : 1 000 000; b) 1 : 10 000; c) 1 : 50 000; d) 1 : 1000.

- **Locus; 15 minutes; page 140**
  Establish what the locus (plural loci) of a point means. Provide the student with several A4 sheets of paper and ask them to mark the point A with a cross in the centre of each sheet. Differentiating the questions according to ability, ask the student to complete the constructions on the activity sheet.

PLENARY ACTIVITY

- **Points on a compass; 5 minutes**
  Draw the four cardinal points on a compass. Ask the student to give you the bearing angle between North and East/South/West. Extend to North-East, South-East, North-West and South-West.

HOMEWORK ACTIVITY

- **Bingo bearings; 15–45 minutes; page 141**
  Ask the student to complete a row, a column or the whole grid, depending on ability.

SUPPORT IDEA

- **Bearings and scale** Using a map of the local area, have a look at the scale and work out the distance between various different pairs of points. Then, invent some imaginary places that the student should mark on the map, given the real distance from a fixed point.

EXTENSION IDEA

Bearings and scale Ask the student to find the bearing from other points, e.g. from A to B. Challenge the student to predict the bearing before measuring it.

PROGRESS AND OBSERVATIONS

137

STARTER ACTIVITY: GINGERBREAD MEN

TIMING: 5 MINS

LEARNING OBJECTIVES

- Use ratios to describe the relationship between up to three quantities

EQUIPMENT

- calculator

1. **Here is the ingredients list for making 12 gingerbread men:**

    100 g butter
    75 g sugar
    225 g flour

    How much of each ingredient would you need to make:

    a) six gingerbread men?

    b) nine gingerbread men?

    c) 14 gingerbread men?

MAIN ACTIVITY: BEARINGS AND SCALE

TIMING: 25 MINS

LEARNING OBJECTIVES

- Interpret maps and scale drawings
- Use bearings

EQUIPMENT

- protractor
- ruler

1. **Work out the actual distance and bearing of each point from X.**

×
E

1:100 000

×
A

×

×
D

×
B

×
C

MATHS
— HIGHER —

Edexcel

MAIN ACTIVITY: LOCUS

TIMING: 15 MINS

LEARNING OBJECTIVES

* Construct scale drawings using loci and bearings

EQUIPMENT

* ruler
* protractor
* pair of compasses
* plain paper

A locus (plural loci) is a set of points that follows a particular rule.

For example, the locus of points 4 cm from point A is a circle with radius 4 cm, as shown in this diagram.

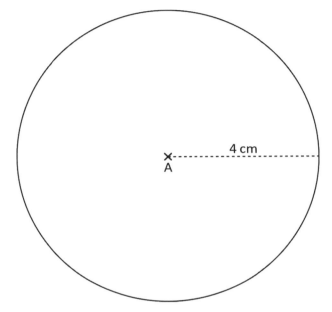

1. **On a separate piece of paper, mark a point in the centre of the page and label it A.**

   a) Mark the points that are on a bearing of 320° from point A.

   b) Using a scale of 1 : 100 000, mark the points that are 3.5 km from A.

   c) Using a scale of 1 : 50 000, shade the area that is more than 4 km from A.

   d) Using a scale of 1 : 1 000 000, mark the point B, 65 km due north of A.

   e) Draw the line AB.

   f) Mark the points that are exactly 30 km from the line AB, using the scale 1 : 1 000 000

   g) Using a scale of 1 : 25 000, mark the point C, 2 km due East of B.

   h) Mark the point D, which is on a bearing of 045° from A and 300° from B.

   i) How far is D from A in kilometres, using the scale 1 : 25 000?

HOMEWORK ACTIVITY: BINGO BEARINGS

TIMING: 15–45 MINS

LEARNING OBJECTIVES
- Measure line segments and angles in geometric figures
- Interpret maps and scale drawings
- Use bearings

EQUIPMENT
- ruler
- protractor

1. **Complete this bingo board of questions. You can complete a row, a column, or even the whole board!**

Work out the bearing of B from A. × A × B	The scale on a map is 1 : 250 000. What does 1 cm on the map represent?	The bearing of A from B is 120°. What is the bearing of B from A?
The distance between Petersfield and Liphook is 16 km. On a map with scale 1 : 200 000, what is the distance between the two towns?	C is on a bearing of 125° from point D. Draw the line on which point C must lie. × D	C is on a bearing of 120° from B and 220° from A. Mark the point C on the diagram. × A × B
Using a scale of 1 : 100 000, mark the locus of points less than 2 km from A. x A	Mark the point C which is on a bearing of 010° from A and 345° from B. B _____ A	Work out the area covered by the locus that is less than 4 cm from a vertical line of length 8 cm. (Hint: Sketch it first!)

21 ANSWERS

STARTER ACTIVITY: GINGERBREAD MEN

1. a) 50 g butter, 37.5 g sugar, 112.5 g flour
b) 75 g butter, 56.25 g sugar, 168.75 g flour
c) 116.7 g butter, 87.5 g sugar, 262.5 g flour

MAIN ACTIVITY: BEARINGS AND SCALE

1. X to A = 050°, 9 km
X to B = 140°, 5 km
X to C = 175°, 10 km
X to D = 245°, 6 km
X to E = 355°, 11 km

MAIN ACTIVITY: LOCUS

1. a)–i) Check the student's drawings are accurate.

HOMEWORK ACTIVITY: BINGO BEARINGS

1.

245°	2.5 km	300°
8 cm	Check the student's solution.	Check the student's solution.
Circle with centre A, radius 2 cm, dotted circumference	Check the student's solution.	$64 + 16\pi = 114.3$ cm^2

GLOSSARY

Bearing
The angle, measured from North, created by joining two points with a straight line

Locus (plural loci)
A set of points that follows a particular rule

22 Ratio, proportion and rates of change: Direct and inverse proportion

Learning objectives

- Solve problems involving direct and inverse proportion, including graphical and algebraic representations

Specification links

- R10, R13

Starter activity

- **How long and how much?; 5 minutes; page 144**
  The questions on this activity sheet introduce the ideas of inverse and direct proportion in a real-life scenario.

Main activities

- **Direct and inverse proportion; 20 minutes; page 145**
  Establish what direct and inverse proportion mean. Stress that it is only direct proportion if when one value is zero, the other value is also zero. Discuss how to identify direct proportion algebraically, graphically and by comparing ratios. Establish how to identify inverse proportion algebraically and graphically.
- **Equations of direct and inverse proportion; 20 minutes; page 146**
  Work through the information and worked example on the activity sheet. Then, support the student through the exam-style questions.

Plenary activity

- **Direct or indirect?; 5 minutes**
  Challenge the student to think of scenarios that involve direct and indirect proportion. Challenge the student to suggest an equation showing direct/indirect proportion and to sketch a graph illustrating them both.

Homework activity

- **Proportion in real life; 30 minutes; page 147**
  The problems are based on real-life scenarios. You may wish to encourage the student to use the unitary method to help with solving the problems. Stress to the student the need for 'common sense' when solving problems involving proportion, e.g. by asking: *Do you expect one thing to increase or decrease as the other increases or decreases?*

Support idea

- **Equations of direct and inverse proportion** Start by working through an example of direct proportion (e.g. when $y = 5$, $x = 2$). Establish the ratio $5 : 2$ and discuss how this can be written in the form $m : 1$ ($2.5 : 1$). Establish that the y value is therefore 2.5 times the x value, which can be written as $y = 2.5x$.

Extension idea

- **Proportion in real life** To extend the idea of proportionality, discuss with the student how you could convert between compound measures – e.g. between m/s and km/hour.

Progress and observations

143

STARTER ACTIVITY: HOW LONG AND HOW MUCH?　　　TIMING: 5 MINS

LEARNING OBJECTIVES

- Solve problems involving direct and inverse proportion

EQUIPMENT

1. It takes four men 3 hours to wash ten elephants. How long will it take to do the job if these numbers of people work on it?

   a) one man

   ----

   b) six men

   ----

2. How long will it take:

   a) four men to wash 20 elephants?

   ----

   b) two men to wash 40 elephants?

   ----

   c) one man to wash five elephants?

   ----

3. If each man charges £15 per hour, how much will the original job cost if these numbers of people work on it?

   a) three men

   ----

   b) one man

   ----

   c) eight men

MAIN ACTIVITY: DIRECT AND INVERSE PROPORTION

TIMING: 20 MINS

LEARNING OBJECTIVES	**EQUIPMENT**
• Solve problems involving direct and inverse proportion, including graphical and algebraic representations	none

1. **Write 'direct proportion', 'inverse proportion' or 'neither' next to each of these scenarios, graphs and equations.**

   a) How much you earn in relation to the number of hours you work   ....

   b) How long a bath takes to fill in relation to the rate of flow of water from the tap   ....

   c) The time it takes to cycle to work in relation to the speed you are moving   ....

   d) The time it takes to mow a lawn in relation to the size of the lawn   ....

e)
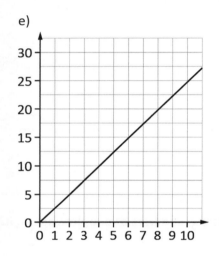

f)
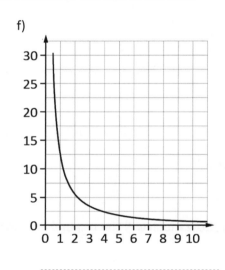

g)
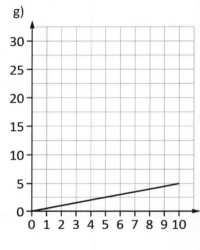

....

   h) $y = 3x$ ....

   i) $y = 10x$ ....

   j) $y = \dfrac{0.3}{x}$ ....

   k) $y = 0.01 + 0.01x$ ....

   l)

x	0	3	5	18	30
y	0	0.3	0.5	1.8	3

....

   m)

x	0	1	2	3	4
y	0	3	5	7	9

....

MATHS
— HIGHER —

MAIN ACTIVITY: EQUATIONS OF DIRECT AND INVERSE PROPORTION   TIMING: 20 MINS

LEARNING OBJECTIVES

- Solve problems involving direct and inverse proportion, including graphical and algebraic representations

EQUIPMENT

If x and y are in direct proportion, then $y \alpha x$ or $y = kx$, where k is a value to be found.

If x and y are in inverse proportion, then $y \alpha \frac{1}{x}$ or $y = \frac{k}{x}$, where k is a value to be found.

Example:

x is in inverse proportion to y. When $x = 3$, $y = 5$. Write an equation connecting x and y.

$$y = \frac{k}{x}$$
$$5 = \frac{k}{3}$$
$$k = 15$$
$$y = \frac{15}{x}$$

---

1. **a is in direct proportion to b. When $a = 0.1$, $b = 5$.**

   a) Find an equation that connects a and b.   ....

   b) Find the value of b when $a = 11$.   ....

2. **m is in inverse proportion to n. When $m = 7$, $n = 12$.**

   a) Find an equation that connects m and n.   ....

   b) Find the value of n when $m = 0.5$.   ....

3. **The time a job takes is in inverse proportion to the number of workmen. If there are 12 workmen, the job will take eight hours.**

   a) Form an equation that links the time taken (T) to the number of workmen (N).

   ....

   b) Use the equation to work out the number of workmen required to do the job in five hours.

   ....

Edexcel

MATHS
— HIGHER —

TUTORS GUILD

HOMEWORK ACTIVITY: PROPORTION IN REAL LIFE

TIMING: 30 MINS

LEARNING OBJECTIVES
* Solve problems involving direct and inverse proportion, including graphical and algebraic representations

EQUIPMENT
none

1. **A brand of plant food must be made into a mixture of 5 ml of feed for every 100 ml of water.**

a) How much food and water would be needed to make 525 ml of the mixture? ....

b) Which equation accurately represents the relationship between the plant food (*F*) and the water (*W*) in the mixture? Circle your answer.

$$F = 20W \qquad W = 20F \qquad F = \frac{20}{W} \qquad W = \frac{20}{F}$$

2. A tap runs at a rate of 12 litres per minute.

a) How long will it take to run a bath that holds 100 litres? ....

b) Work out the rate of flow in litres per hour. ....

c) 1 litre ≈ 4.62 gallons. Work out the rate of flow in gallons per hour. Give your answer to 3 significant figures. ....

3. A bank offers an exchange rate of £1 = $1.30.

a) Work out how many dollars you would get for £500. ....

b) How many GBP would you get for $400? Give your answer to 2 decimal places. ....

c) A pair of jeans costs £50 in the UK and $60 in America. Where is it cheaper? Show all your calculations. ....

d) Write an equation that links pounds (*P*) to dollars (*D*). ....

4. This graph shows water cooling over time.

a) Use the graph to work out the temperature of the water 10 minutes after it was boiled.

....

b) Describe in words the relationship between the temperature of the water and time after it has boiled.

....

c) It is assumed that the temperature of tea is in inverse proportion to the time after the tea is made. Use your answer to part a) to form an equation linking temperature (*C*) to time in minutes (*T*).

....

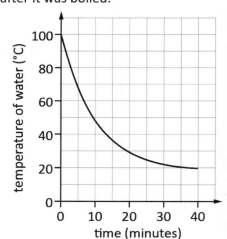

22 ANSWERS

STARTER ACTIVITY: HOW LONG AND HOW MUCH?

1. a) 12 hours   b) 2 hours
2. a) 6 hours   b) 24 hours   c) 6 hours
3. a) £180   b) £180   c) £180

MAIN ACTIVITY: DIRECT AND INVERSE PROPORTION

1. a) direct   b) inverse   c) inverse   d) direct
   e) direct   f) inverse   g) direct   h) direct
   i) direct   j) inverse   k) neither   l) direct   m) neither

MAIN ACTIVITY: EQUATIONS OF DIRECT AND INVERSE PROPORTION

1. a) $a = 0.02b$ or $b = 50a$ b) 550

2. a) $m = \dfrac{84}{n}$ or $n = \dfrac{84}{m}$ b) 168

3. a) $T = \dfrac{96}{N}$ or $N = \dfrac{96}{T}$ b) 19.2; would need to hire 20 workmen

HOMEWORK ACTIVITY: PROPORTION IN REAL LIFE

1. a) 25 ml feed, 500 ml water   b) $W = 20F$
2. a) 8 minutes 20 seconds   b) 720 litres per hour   c) 156 gallons per hour
3. a) $650   b) £307.69   c) 50 × 1.3 = $65, so $5 cheaper in America
   d) $D = 1.3P$
4. a) 46–48 °C
   b) As the time after boiling increases, the temperature of the water decreases, so the two things are in inverse proportion.
   c) $T = \dfrac{490}{C}$ or $C = \dfrac{490}{T}$

GLOSSARY

Direct proportion
Two variables are in direct proportion if, when one increases, the other increases by the same percentage.
An equation relating the two is of the form $y = kx$, where k is constant.

Inverse proportion
Two variables are in inverse proportion if, when one increases, the other decreases. An equation relating the two is of the
form $y = \dfrac{k}{x}$, where k is constant.

23 RATIO, PROPORTION AND RATES OF CHANGE: RATES OF CHANGE

LEARNING OBJECTIVES	SPECIFICATION LINKS

LEARNING OBJECTIVES

- Interpret the gradient of straight line graphs that illustrate direct and inverse proportion
- Set up, solve and interpret the answers in growth and decay problems, including compound interest

SPECIFICATION LINKS

- R14, R16, A10, A14

STARTER ACTIVITY

- **Finding percentages; 5 minutes; page 150**
  The student must complete this activity without using a calculator.

MAIN ACTIVITIES

- **Interpreting graphs; 20 minutes; page 151**
  Discuss that the gradient represents rate of change. Explain that this means different things depending on what the graph represents. Ask the student to work through question 1, looking at linear rates of change. Then ask the student to move on to question 2, modelling how to find the average rate of change by finding the gradient of a chord joining two points, and instantaneous rate of change by finding the gradient of a tangent at a point.

- **Growth and decay; 20 minutes; page 152**
  Introduce the idea of growth and decay and explain the difference between compound and simple interest. Ask the student to work through question 1. Then challenge the student to suggest a way to calculate the amount in the account after three years without doing three repeated calculations. Ask the student to complete the remaining questions.

PLENARY ACTIVITY

- **Sketching graphs; 5 minutes**
  Ask the student to sketch two graphs: one showing growth and one showing decay.

HOMEWORK ACTIVITY

- **Exam-style questions; 30 minutes; page 153**
  Full instructions are given on the activity sheet.

SUPPORT IDEAS

- **Interpreting graphs** When considering the gradient of the graph, remind the student that they are finding a change in the 'y' value for a change of 1 in the 'x' value. Encourage them to think logically about what is changing over time, and to express their answer in 'real-life' terms.
- **Growth and decay** Encourage the student to draw up a table of values when calculating compound interest.

EXTENSION IDEA

- **Growth and decay** Challenge the student to write iterative formulae for questions 1, 2 and 3.

PROGRESS AND OBSERVATIONS

STARTER ACTIVITY: FINDING PERCENTAGES

TIMING: 5 MINS

LEARNING OBJECTIVES

- Find percentages using mental methods

EQUIPMENT

1. **A shop puts on a sale. They allow customers to decide between two offers: 40% off one item, or 20% off their entire bill.**

   Here are the full prices of three items in the sale:

   - DVD player £80

   - Bluetooth speaker £125

   - Record player £250

   a) Erica buys all three items. Which is the better deal for her?

   ----

   b) Malcolm buys one item at the sale. He gets a set of headphones for £48.
      What was the original price of the headphones?

MAIN ACTIVITY: INTERPRETING GRAPHS   TIMING: 20 MINS

LEARNING OBJECTIVES

- Interpret the gradient of a straight line graph as rate of change

EQUIPMENT

 1. **For each scenario, find the gradient of the graph. Explain what the gradient represents and the units it is measured in.**

a)

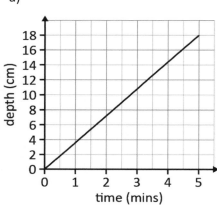

b)

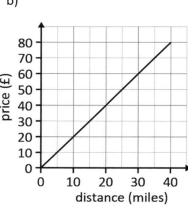

c)

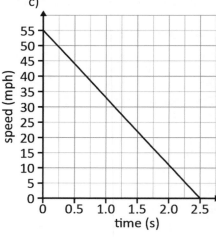

....

....

d)   Do any of the graphs show direct proportion? For those that do, find the equation of the graph.

2. **A scientist carries out an experiment. She records the volume of a chemical that has been left to evaporate over a period of 10 hours. Use the graph to work out:**

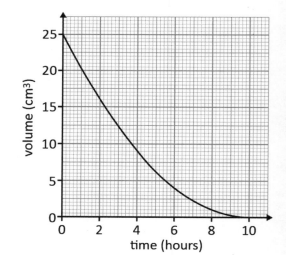

a)   the average rate of decrease in volume over the 10 hours

....

b)   the instantaneous rate of decrease in volume at several different times.

....

....

MAIN ACTIVITY: GROWTH AND DECAY

TIMING: 20 MINS

LEARNING OBJECTIVES

- Set up, solve and interpret the answers in growth and decay problems including compound interest

EQUIPMENT

- graph paper
- calculator

1. A scientist estimates that the number of insects in a colony halves each year. Initially, there are 3.5×10^3 insects in the colony. Which of the following equations could be used to work out the number of insects in the colony after n years? Circle your answer and explain your reason to your tutor.

$$\frac{1}{2}n(3.5 \times 10^3) \qquad \frac{1}{2}^n (3.5 \times 10^3) \qquad (3.5 \times 10^3) + \frac{1}{2}n$$

2. A bank account offers 5% compound interest per year on deposits of £1000 or more. Erin invests £1000 at the bank.

   a) Calculate how much she will have in the bank after:

   i) 1 year .... ii) 2 years .... iii) 3 years ....

   b) Complete this table.

Years invested	0	1	2	3	4	5	6
Total in account	£1000						

   c) On a separate piece of paper, draw a suitable pair of axes and plot the graph to show the amount Erin will have in her bank account over a six-year period.

   d) How long will it be before Erin has over £1500 in the bank? ....

   e) Write a formula connecting the amount in the bank (S) with the number of years the money has been invested (n).

---

3. The value of a car depreciates by 5% per annum. The original price of the car was £48 000.

   a) Form an equation that can be used to calculate the value after x years. ....

   b) Use your formula to work out the value after 10 years. ....

4. An iterative formula is used to calculate the amount in a bank account: $d_0 = £300$, $d_{t+1} = 1.03 \, d_t$.

   a) Work out the values of d_1, d_2 and d_3. ....

   b) The initial deposit in the bank was £300. What is the interest rate of the account?

MATHS
— HIGHER —

HOMEWORK ACTIVITY: EXAM-STYLE QUESTIONS   TIMING: 30 MINS

LEARNING OBJECTIVES

- Set up, solve and interpret the answers in growth and decay problems including compound interest

EQUIPMENT

1. The number of hits on a website increases over time. Erica estimates that the number of hits increases by 10% each day. On day 1, the website had 2500 hits.

   How many hits would it have on day 4?

   ....

   (3 marks)

2. **Mr Bland invests £3000 in a motorbike. Its value depreciates at a rate of 13% per annum.**

   a) How much will it be worth in 3 years' time? Give your answer to the nearest pound.

   ....

   (3 marks)

   b) Given y = value of motorbike and x = time in years, write an equation linking y and x.

   ....

   (2 marks)

   c) How long before Mr Bland's investment is worth less than half of what he originally invested?

   ....

   (2 marks)

3. An investor plots the graph below to show the increase in value of her investments over a three-year period.

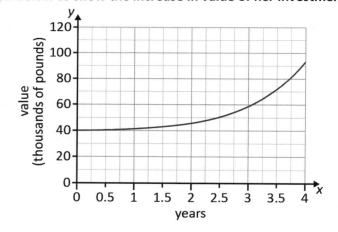

   Use the graph to work out:

   a) the average rate of increase in value over the 4 years, to the nearest thousand   ....

   b) the instantaneous rate of increase in value at 3 years, to the nearest thousand.   ....

   (4 marks)

23 ANSWERS

STARTER ACTIVITY: FINDING PERCENTAGES

1. a) Taking 40% off the most expensive item gives a price of £355. Taking 20% off the whole bill gives a price of £364. 40% off one item is the better deal.
b) The headphones originally cost £80.

MAIN ACTIVITY: INTERPRETING GRAPHS

1. a) Rate of flow of water in cm/minute; gradient = 3.6 cm/minute
b) Cost per mile or rate of increase in cost in pounds/mile; gradient = £2 per mile
c) Deceleration or rate of change of speed in mph/s; gradient = 22 mph/s
d) Parts a) and b) show direct proportion: graph a) $y = 3.6x$; graph b) $y = 2x$
2. a) -2.5 cm^3/hour
b) Answers will vary depending on where the tangents are drawn.

MAIN ACTIVITY: GROWTH AND DECAY

1. a) $\frac{1}{2}^n (3.5 \times 10^3)$

2. a) i) £1050   ii) £1102.50   iii) £1157.63

b)

Years invested	0	1	2	3	4	5	6
Total in account	£1000.00	£1050.00	£1102.50	£1157.63	£1215.51	£1276.28	£1340.10

c) Check the student's graph.
d) 9 years
e) $S = 1000 \times (1.05^n)$
3. a) value = $48\,000 \times 0.95^n$ b) £28 739
4. a) $d_1 = 309$, $d_2 = 318.27$, $d_3 = 327.82$ b) 3%

HOMEWORK ACTIVITY: EXAM-STYLE QUESTIONS

1. 3327
2. a) £1976   b) $y = 3000 \times 0.87^x$ c) 5 years
3. a) 14 thousand per year   b) 20 thousand per year

GLOSSARY

Compound interest
Interest calculated on the original sum invested and the interest earned

Simple interest
Interest calculated on the original sum invested

24 GEOMETRY AND MEASURES: ANGLES

LEARNING OBJECTIVES

- Apply the properties of angles at a point, on a line, vertically opposite, corresponding and alternate
- Calculate and use the sum of angles in polygons

SPECIFICATION LINKS

- G1, G3

STARTER ACTIVITY

- **Colour it in; 5 minutes; page 156**
  Full instructions are given on the activity sheet.

MAIN ACTIVITIES

- **Using angle properties; 15 minutes; page 157**
  Remind the student of the properties of: angles on a straight line, angles around a point, angles in a triangle, vertically opposite angles, corresponding angles and alternate angles. Draw diagrams to demonstrate these. Ask the student to work through the activity.

- **Polygons; 25 minutes; page 158**
  Remind the student that for each 'additional side', you add 180° to the sum of the internal angles. If necessary, show this by splitting a polygon into triangles. Remind the student that the sum of the external angles is always 360°. If necessary, model this on a polygon. The questions require discussion rather than written work. Encourage the student to communicate using the correct mathematical terms and by illustrating the discussion with diagrams.

PLENARY ACTIVITY

- **How many facts?; 5 minutes**
  Give the student five minutes to write down all of the facts they can remember about angles.

HOMEWORK ACTIVITY

- **Flash cards/Poster; 30 minutes; page 159**
  Full instructions are given on the activity sheet. Encourage the student to make their flash cards or poster bright and engaging so they will want to display it or use it for revision as they get closer to their exam.

SUPPORT IDEAS

- **Using angle properties** When solving problems of this form, encourage the student to mark all of the angles they know, rather than just trying to find the missing angles.
- **Flash cards/Poster** You may wish to support the student by providing illustrated 'fact cards' of the angle properties they can use, and asking them to use these to create a poster.

EXTENSION IDEA

- **Polygons** Challenge the student to find regular polygons that tessellate (one or a combination of two), justifying their suggestions.

PROGRESS AND OBSERVATIONS

STARTER ACTIVITY: COLOUR IT IN

TIMING: 5 MINS

LEARNING OBJECTIVES

• Use conventional terms and notation

EQUIPMENT

• coloured pencils
• protractor

1. **On shape ABCDE below, colour:**

   • side AB red
   • angle BCD green
   • a pair of parallel sides blue
   • a pair of perpendicular sides yellow
   • a right angle orange
   • an acute angle pink
   • an obtuse angle orange.

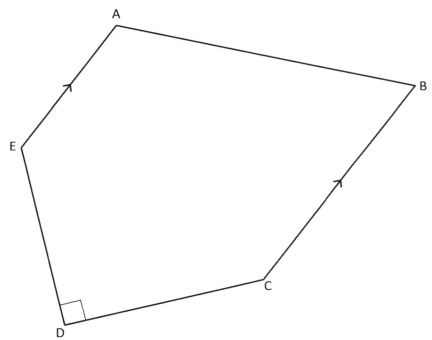

2. **What is the name of shape ABCDE?** --

3. **The sum of the angles in shape ABCDE is 540°. Given <DEA = 2<ABC, <EAB = 3<ABC and <EAB = <BCD, form and solve an equation to find the size of each of the angles.**

   Hint: Set <ABC = x.

MAIN ACTIVITY: USING ANGLE PROPERTIES   **TIMING: 15 MINS**

LEARNING OBJECTIVES

* Apply the properties of angles at a point, on a line, vertically opposite, corresponding and alternate

EQUIPMENT

* calculator

 1. **Calculate the size of the angles labelled *a* to *g*.**
   For each angle, explain your reasoning to your tutor using the correct vocabulary.

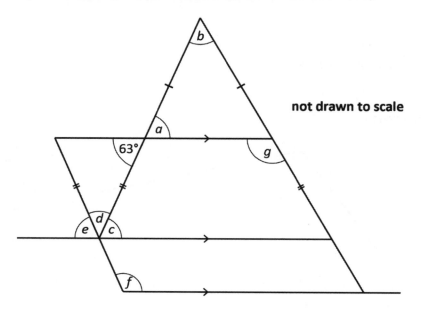

not drawn to scale

---

 2. **Prove that *a* + *b* = *c*.**

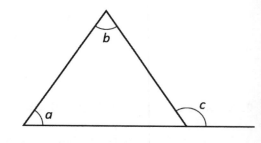

---

 3. **B is on a bearing of 050° from A. C is on a bearing of 110° from B. Given that AB = BC, work out the bearing of A from C.**

MAIN ACTIVITY: POLYGONS

TIMING: 25 MINS

LEARNING OBJECTIVES

- Calculate and use the sum of angles in polygons

EQUIPMENT

1. **Complete this table.**

Name of shape	Number of sides	Sum of interior angles	Sum of exterior angles
triangle	3	180°	360°
quadrilateral	4	360°	
pentagon	5		
hexagon	6		
heptagon	7		
octagon	8		
nonagon	9		
decagon	10		

2. **Discuss the answers to each of these questions with your tutor. Make some notes below.**

a) How could you find the sum of the internal angles of an *n*-sided polygon?

----

b) How could you find the sum of the external angles of an *n*-sided polygon?

----

c) One of the external angles of a regular polygon is 20°. How many sides does it have?

----

d) One of the internal angles of a regular polygon is 140°. How many sides does it have?

----

e) Explain how you know that regular octagons and squares tessellate.

----

f) Explain how you know that pentagons and nonagons will not tessellate.

----

g) In a regular polygon, the ratio of the size of the exterior angle to the interior angle is 1 : 9. How many sides does the polygon have?

HOMEWORK ACTIVITY: FLASH CARDS/POSTER

TIMING: 30 MINS

LEARNING OBJECTIVES

- Apply the properties of angles at a point, on a line, vertically opposite, corresponding and alternate
- Calculate and use the sum of angles in polygons

EQUIPMENT

- index cards/large sheet of paper
- coloured pens
- ruler

 1. **There are many facts about angles that you will need to remember for the exam. Make either a set of flash cards or a large poster listing all the facts you have covered during this lesson.**

Include facts about:

- angles on a straight line

- angles around a point

- angles in a triangle

- vertically opposite angles

- corresponding angles

- alternate angles

- angles in a quadrilateral

- angles in a polygon

- sum of exterior angles of a polygon

- angles in a regular polygon.

24 ANSWERS

STARTER ACTIVITY: COLOUR IT IN

1. Check student's drawing.
2. pentagon
3. <ABC = 50°, <DEA = 100°, <EAB = <BCD = 150°

MAIN ACTIVITY: USING ANGLE PROPERTIES

1. a = 63° because vertically opposite angles are equal

b = 54° because angles in a triangle add up to 180° and the two angles at the base of equal sides in an isosceles triangle are equal

c = 63° because alternate angles are equal

d = 54° because the two angles at the base of equal sides in an isosceles triangle are equal and angles in a triangle sum to 180°

e = 63° because angles on a straight line sum to 180°

f = 117° because corresponding angles are equal

g = 117° because angles on a straight line sum to 180°

2. The sum of the angles in a triangle = 180 °, therefore:

$c = 180° - (180° - (a + b))$

$c = a + b$

3. 260°

MAIN ACTIVITY: POLYGONS

1.

Name of shape	Number of sides	Sum of interior angles	Sum of exterior angles
triangle	3	180°	360°
quadrilateral	4	360°	360°
pentagon	5	540°	360°
hexagon	6	720°	360°
heptagon	7	900°	360°
octagon	8	1080°	360°
nonagon	9	1260°	360°
decagon	10	1440°	360°

2. a) $(n - 2) \times 180°$ or two less than the number of sides multiplied by 180°.

b) The external angles of all polygons add up to 360°.

c) 360° ÷ 20 = 18   d) (180 – 140) = 40; 360 ÷ 40 = 9

e) The internal angle of a regular octagon is 135°. You could put two octagons together with one square at each vertex, since 135 + 135 + 90 = 360°, as shown in the diagram.

f) The internal angle of a pentagon is 108°, and the internal angle of a nonagon it is 140°. No combination of these will add up to 360°.

g) 20 sides

HOMEWORK ACTIVITY: FLASH CARDS/POSTER

1. Check the student's work.

GLOSSARY

Parallel
Two lines are parallel if they have the same distance continually between them.

Perpendicular
Two lines are perpendicular if the angle between them is 90°.

25 GEOMETRY AND MEASURES: 2-D SHAPES

LEARNING OBJECTIVES	SPECIFICATION LINKS
• Derive and apply the properties of quadrilaterals, triangles and other plane figures	• G1, G2, G4, G6, A8, A9, A17, A21

STARTER ACTIVITY

• **Properties of a triangle; 5 minutes; page 162**
Full instructions are given on the activity sheet. You may wish to encourage the student to sketch the triangles, marking any equal sides or angles.

MAIN ACTIVITIES

• **Properties of quadrilaterals; 20 minutes; page 163**
Brainstorm what the student already knows about quadrilaterals, including parallel/perpendicular sides, angles, diagonals (are they perpendicular?), lines of symmetry, and the sum of their interior/exterior angles. Work through the questions, discussing the student's answers.

• **Constructions; 20 minutes; page 164**
Note that the student is expected to be able to construct SSS, SAS and ASA triangles using a protractor, pair of compasses and ruler. You may wish to check they are confident with this before embarking on the main activity. When tackling the exam-style questions in part B, remind the student that the construction they will be asked to do will be one of the five constructions they have covered in part A. For exam-style question 1, explain to the student that in an exam, they will usually be given the first construction line (you could draw line AB for them).

PLENARY ACTIVITY

• **How many?; 5 minutes**
Ask the student to decide how many types of quadrilateral there are that:
a) contain a right angle   b) have at least one pair of parallel sides   c) contain an obtuse angle.

HOMEWORK ACTIVITY

• **Construction vlogger; 60 minutes; page 165**
Full instructions are given on the activity sheet.

SUPPORT IDEAS

• **Properties of quadrilaterals** Describe the quadrilateral to the student while he or she sketches it.
• **Constructions** The questions in part B (exam-style questions) can be set as homework.

EXTENSION IDEA

• **Properties of quadrilaterals** Give the student two coordinates of the vertices of a particular type of quadrilateral. Ask them to suggest all possible pairs of coordinates where the other two vertices could be.

PROGRESS AND OBSERVATIONS

STARTER ACTIVITY: PROPERTIES OF A TRIANGLE

TIMING: 5 MINS

LEARNING OBJECTIVES

- Know the properties of types of triangle

EQUIPMENT

1. **Match each statement below to at least one of the types of triangle listed. Some statements will apply to more than one triangle.**

A: All angles are equal.

B: Two angles are equal.

C: No angles are equal.

D: May contain a right angle   scalene triangle

E: All sides have equal length.

F: Two sides have equal length.   isosceles triangle

G: No sides have equal length.

H: Has no lines of symmetry

I: Has one line of symmetry   equilateral triangle

J: Has three lines of symmetry

K: The sum of the internal angles is 180˚.

MAIN ACTIVITY: PROPERTIES OF QUADRILATERALS   TIMING: 20 MINS

LEARNING OBJECTIVES	EQUIPMENT
• Recall and use the properties and definitions of quadrilaterals	none

 1. Sort the statements below into the correct columns of this table.

Always true	Sometimes true	Never true

a) A quadrilateral contains a right angle.

b) A rhombus contains a right angle.

c) A trapezium contains a right angle.

d) A parallelogram contains two obtuse angles.

e) A kite contains two equal angles.

f) The sides of a rhombus are equal.

g) A quadrilateral has one pair of equal sides.

 2. Quadrilateral ABCD has two pairs of sides of equal length. The diagonals are perpendicular. What is the name of the quadrilateral?

....

 3. In a quadrilateral, <ABC = 2<BCD, <CDA = 3<BCD and <DAB = <BCD + 10. Hint: Set <BCD = *x*.

a) Write an algebraic expression for the size of each of the other angles.

....

b) Form and solve an equation to find the size of the largest angle in the quadrilateral.

....

4. On the coordinate grid, plot the points: A (5, 3), B (4, 6) and C (1, 7). The points A, B and C are three vertices of a kite.

 a) Write FOUR possible pairs of coordinates for the vertex D.

 b) Draw a straight line on the axes, indicating the possible positions of D.

 c) Work out the equation of the line going through these points.

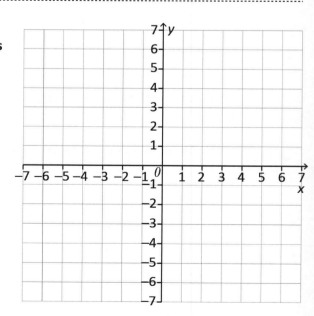

MAIN ACTIVITY: CONSTRUCTIONS

TIMING: 20 MINS

LEARNING OBJECTIVES

- Use standard ruler and compass constructions

EQUIPMENT

- pair of compasses
- ruler
- protractor
- sharp pencil
- plain paper

Part A: Constructions

1. On a separate piece of paper, draw a line 10 cm long. Label the line AB. Construct the perpendicular bisector of the line AB.

2. Draw a line 12 cm long. Label the line CD. Mark with a cross a point anywhere on the paper, not on the line CD. From that point, construct a perpendicular to the line CD.

3. Use a protractor to draw <ABC with size 80°. Construct the bisector of <ABC.

4. Construct an angle of 90°.

5. Construct an angle of 45°.

Part B: Exam-style questions

6. Use a pair of compasses and a ruler to construct triangle ABC with AB = 12 cm, <CAB = 62° and <ABC = 35°. You must show all your construction lines.

7. Construct the bisector of the angle XYZ:

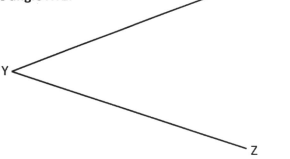

8. In the rectangle ABCD, where AB = 6 cm and BC = 5 cm, shade the area that is both less than 4 cm from A and closer to BC than AD.

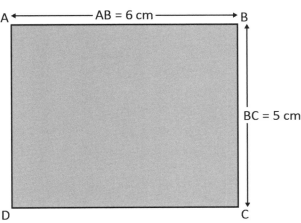

HOMEWORK ACTIVITY: CONSTRUCTION VLOGGER

TIMING: 60 MINS

LEARNING OBJECTIVES
- Use standard ruler and compass construction
- Construct figures and solve loci problems

EQUIPMENT
- technology with filming capacity (phone, tablet, PC, laptop)

1. **You are going to become a construction vlogger. Make a video (or write a script with diagrams) showing other GCSE maths students how to construct the following:**

   a) a perpendicular bisector to a line

   b) an angle bisector

   c) a perpendicular from a point to a line

   d) a right angle

   e) a 45° angle

   f) a locus of points a fixed distance from a point

   g) a locus of points a fixed distance from a line.

   If you need help, look at videos that are already available online.

25 ANSWERS

STARTER ACTIVITY: PROPERTIES OF A TRIANGLE

1. scalene triangle: C, D, G, H, K   isosceles triangle: B, D, F, I, K   equilateral triangle: A, E, J, K

MAIN ACTIVITY: PROPERTIES OF QUADRILATERALS

1.

Always true	Sometimes true	Never true
A parallelogram contains two obtuse angles. A kite contains two equal angles. The sides of a rhombus are equal.	A quadrilateral contains a right angle. A trapezium contains a right angle. A quadrilateral has one pair of equal sides.	A rhombus contains a right angle.

2. kite
3. a) $\angle ABC = 2x$, $\angle CDA = 3x$, $\angle DAB = x + 10$
b) $7x + 10 = 360$ so $x = 50$; largest angle = $\angle CDA = 150°$
4. a) any coordinates on the line $y = x + 2$
b) See grid opposite
c) $y = x + 2$

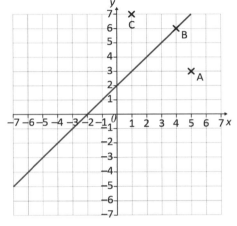

MAIN ACTIVITY: CONSTRUCTIONS

1–8. Check student's constructions using a ruler and protractor where required.

HOMEWORK ACTIVITY: CONSTRUCTION VLOGGER

1. Check the student's video.

GLOSSARY

Diagonal of a quadrilateral
The straight line joining opposite vertices

Locus (plural loci)
A region or set of points that satisfy particular criteria

26 GEOMETRY AND MEASURES: PERIMETER, AREA AND VOLUME

LEARNING OBJECTIVES

- Know and apply formulae to calculate area of triangles, parallelograms and trapezia
- Calculate the surface area of cubes, cuboids, prisms and cylinders
- Know and apply formulae for volume of cubes, cuboids and prisms

SPECIFICATION LINKS

- G16, G17, G18, G20

STARTER ACTIVITY

- **Units of measure; 5 minutes; page 168**
  Full instructions are given on the activity sheet. Discuss with the student which units are easy to identify and why.

MAIN ACTIVITIES

- **Perimeter and area; 25 minutes; page 169**
  Remind the student of the definitions of perimeter and area. Work through the table and complete the formula for the area of each shape. Mark the relevant diagrams with the dimensions that are referred to.
  Move on to calculating compound and surface areas. You may wish to show the student physical objects to help them calculate the surface area of each 3-D shape. The student is given the formula for the surface area of a sphere and a cone on the formula page at the front of the exam, but needs to be familiar with using them. Parts f) and g) of question 2 will require the use of Pythagoras' theorem to work out missing lengths.
- **Calculating volume; 15 minutes; page 170**
  Review what volume means and discuss the formula for calculating the volume of any prism. Work through the example, calculating the volume of the cylinder. Explain that the exact area of the cross-section is written – the solution is not rounded until the final stage. For question 2, tell the student that shape b) is called a frustum.

PLENARY ACTIVITY

- **How could I?; 5 minutes**
  Ask the student to explain to you how to find the volume of different 3-D shapes.
  Differentiate according to the student's ability.

HOMEWORK ACTIVITY

- **Spider diagram; 60 minutes; page 171**
  Full instructions are given on the activity sheet. Encourage the student to include as much information on the spider diagram as possible.

SUPPORT IDEA

- **Perimeter and area** When calculating surface area, sketch a net of each shape before attempting to find the surface area. You could also provide the student with shapes they can manipulate to help them work out how many different shapes they need to calculate the area. When finding the surface area of a cylinder, it helps to show that the curved side is actually a rectangle by peeling the label from a tin of soup or similar.

EXTENSION IDEAS

- **Perimeter and area** Challenge the student to find the surface area of a triangular prism that has a cross-section of an equilateral triangle with sides of length 10. They will need to use Pythagoras' theorem to find the height of the triangle before finding the surface area.
- **Calculating volume** Extend finding the volume of the shapes in cm^3 to working out how many litres each shape will hold.

PROGRESS AND OBSERVATIONS

STARTER ACTIVITY: UNITS OF MEASURE

TIMING: 5 MINS

LEARNING OBJECTIVES

- Know units of length, area and volume

EQUIPMENT

1. **All the units in the cloud are measures of length, area or volume. Write them in the correct column in the table below.**

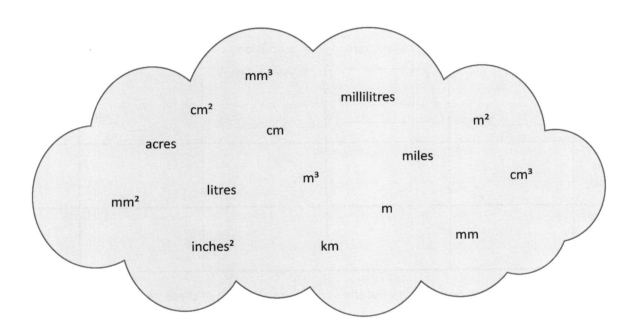

Length	Area	Volume

MAIN ACTIVITY: PERIMETER AND AREA

TIMING: 25 MINS

LEARNING OBJECTIVES

- Know and apply formulae to calculate the areas of triangles, parallelograms, trapezia, circles and sectors
- Calculate the surface area of 3-D shapes

EQUIPMENT

- card
- scissors
- glue

1. **Write the formula for calculating the area of each of these shapes. Mark any dimensions you refer to on the diagrams. Once complete, cut out the table and stick it onto card. You need to remember these formulae!**

Shape	triangle	parallelogram	trapezium	circle	sector
Formula for area					
Formula for perimeter					

2. **Explain to your tutor how you would work out the surface area of each of these shapes.**

    Hint: To work out the surface area of a 3-D shape, you could sketch the net to see how many faces there are and what shape each face is.

a)
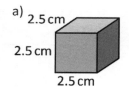
2.5 cm
2.5 cm
2.5 cm

b)
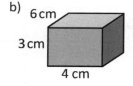
6 cm
3 cm
4 cm

c)
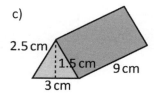
2.5 cm
1.5 cm
9 cm
3 cm

d)
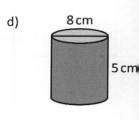
8 cm
5 cm

e)
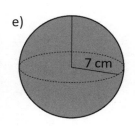
7 cm

f)
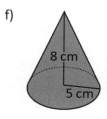
8 cm
5 cm

g)
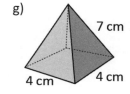
7 cm
4 cm
4 cm

h)

12 cm

3. **Now work them out! Write your answers on the line below each shape.**

MATHS
— HIGHER —

TUTORS' GUILD

Edexcel

MAIN ACTIVITY: CALCULATING VOLUME

TIMING: 15 MINS

LEARNING OBJECTIVES
- Know and apply formulae for volume of cubes, cuboids, prisms, cylinders, spheres, pyramids, cones

EQUIPMENT
- calculator

Example:

Calculate the exact volume of this cylinder to the nearest cm³.

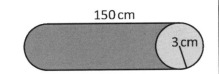

150 cm

3 cm

cross-sectional area = π × 3²

= 9π

volume = 150 × 9π

= 1350π cm³

---

1. Write the formula for calculating the volume of each of these shapes. Mark any dimensions you refer to on the diagrams.

Cuboid	Prism	Cylinder	Sphere	Pyramid	Cone

2. Explain how you could calculate the volume of each of these shapes.

a)  ....

....

b)  ....

....

c)  ....

....

HOMEWORK ACTIVITY: SPIDER DIAGRAM

TIMING: 60 MINS

LEARNING OBJECTIVES

- Know and apply formulae for volume of cubes, cuboids, prisms, spheres, pyramids, cones
- Know and apply formulae to calculate area of triangles, parallelograms, trapezia, circles and sectors
- Calculate the surface area of 3-D shapes

EQUIPMENT

- large sheet of paper

1. **Draw a spider diagram to display all the information you have learned about calculating areas and volumes.**

   Ensure that you include:

   - how to calculate the area of squares, rectangles, circles, triangles, parallelograms, trapezoids (a quadrilateral with no parallel sides) and sectors

   - how to calculate the volume of cubes, cuboids, cylinders, prisms, spheres, pyramids, cones, hemispheres and frustums

   - how to calcuate the surface area of cubes, cuboids, cylinders, triangular prisms, spheres, pyramids, cones and hemispheres

   - which unit should be used for each measurement.

   Try to show where concepts link. You may wish to include some examples.

26 ANSWERS

STARTER ACTIVITY: UNITS OF MEASURE

1.

Length	Area	Volume
cm	m^2	mm^3
miles	cm^2	millilitres
m	acres	cm^3
km	mm^2	m^3
mm	$inches^2$	litres

MAIN ACTIVITY: PERIMETER AND AREA

1.

Shape	triangle	parallelogram	trapezium	circle	sector
Formula for area	$\frac{1}{2} \times b \times h$	$b \times h$	$h(a + b)$	πr^2	$\frac{\theta}{360}\pi r^2$
Formula for perimeter	$a + b + c$	$2a + 2b$	$a + b + c + d$	$2\pi r$ or πd	$\frac{\theta}{180}\pi r^2 + 2r$

3. a) 37.5 cm^2 b) 108 cm^2 c) 72 cm^2

d) 226.2 cm^2 e) 615.8 cm^2 f) 226.7 cm^2

g) 69.7 cm^2 h) 339.3 cm^2

MAIN ACTIVITY: CALCULATING VOLUME

1.

Cuboid	Prism	Cylinder	Sphere	Pyramid	Cone
$b \times h \times w$	area of cross-section × length	$\pi r^2 h$	$\frac{4}{3}\pi r^3$	$\frac{1}{3}$ area of base × height	$\frac{1}{3}$ area of base × height

2. a) Area of triangular face × length

b) Find the volume of the full cone, then calculate the volume of the smaller cone which has been removed from the top, and subtract the second volume from the first.

c) Add together the volume of the hemisphere and the volume of the cylinder.

HOMEWORK ACTIVITY: SPIDER DIAGRAM

1. Check the student's work.

GLOSSARY

Cross-sectional area
The shape made when a 3-D shape is cut through by a plane

27 GEOMETRY AND MEASURES: PYTHAGORAS' THEOREM

LEARNING OBJECTIVES

- Know the formula for Pythagoras' theorem and apply it to find lengths and angles in right-angled triangles

SPECIFICATION LINKS

- N3, N6, N7, N8, G6, G20

STARTER ACTIVITY

- **Triangle construction; 10 minutes; page 174**
  Remind the student how to construct a triangle given three sides before asking them to construct the triangles described on the activity sheet.

MAIN ACTIVITIES

- **Introducing Pythagoras' theorem; 15 minutes; page 175**
  Model how to find the hypotenuse of a right-angled triangle using Pythagoras' theorem. Ask the student to work through questions 1 and 2. Explain to the student that a number can be left in surd form if you need to give the exact solution. When tackling question 4, you may wish to draw out the cube on scrap paper or make a model of the cube to help the student visualise the problem.
- **Applying Pythagoras' theorem; 20 minutes; page 176**
  Full instructions are given on the activity sheet.

PLENARY ACTIVITY

- **Approximate solution; 5 minutes**
  Draw a right-angled triangle with the two shortest sides both labelled 3 cm. Invite the student to estimate the length of the longest side, then check with a calculator.

HOMEWORK ACTIVITY

- **Explain how…; 60 minutes; page 177**
  Full instructions are given on the activity sheet.

SUPPORT IDEA

- **Introducing Pythagoras' theorem** Before starting on this activity, draw a right-angled triangle with sides of lengths 3, 4 and 5 units. Draw the square out on each side, illustrating the principal before introducing the formula.
  For question 2, support the student by writing the first line of the calculation, e.g. $10^2 + b^2 = 26^2$. Encourage the student to evaluate 10^2 and 26^2 before attempting to solve the equation.

EXTENSION IDEA

- **Applying Pythagoras' theorem** Ask the student to explain how to find the length of a line joining any two points on the coordinate grid.

PROGRESS AND OBSERVATIONS

STARTER ACTIVITY: TRIANGLE CONSTRUCTION

TIMING: 10 MINS

LEARNING OBJECTIVES

- Construct triangles, given three sides

EQUIPMENT

- pair of compasses
- ruler
- protractor
- plain paper

1. Construct triangles with sides of these lengths on a separate sheet of paper.

   a) AB = 5 cm, BC = 3 cm, CA = 4 cm

   b) AB = 5 cm, BC = 13 cm, AC = 12 cm

   c) AB = 6 cm, BC = 8 cm, AC = 10 cm

2. What do you notice about all these triangles?

----

3. Are the triangles congruent or similar? Explain your answer.

MAIN ACTIVITY: INTRODUCING PYTHAGORAS' THEOREM   TIMING: 15 MINS

LEARNING OBJECTIVES

- Know the formula for Pythagoras' theorem and apply it to find lengths

EQUIPMENT

- calculator
- ruler

1. **You can find the lengths of right-angled triangles using Pythagoras' theorem.**

   a) Complete the formula for Pythagoras' theorem: $a^2 +$ .... $=$ ....

   b) Which letter represents the longest side?   ....

2. **Draw any right-angled triangle.**

   a) Measure the length of two of the sides.   ....

   b) Calculate the length of the third side.   ....

   c) Check your answer by measuring.   ....

   d) Repeat, this time calculating a different side.   ....

3. **Work out the length of the diagonal of each shape below. Give the exact answer.**

   a)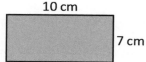

   b)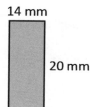

   c)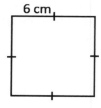

   ....

4. **Cube ABCDEF has sides of length 5 cm.**

   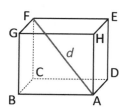

   a) Calculate the length of AE.

   ....

   b) Calculate the length of d.

   ....

MATHS
— HIGHER —

MAIN ACTIVITY: APPLYING PYTHAGORAS' THEOREM   **TIMING: 20 MINS**

LEARNING OBJECTIVES

- Know the formula for Pythagoras' theorem and apply it to find lengths and angles of right-angled triangles

EQUIPMENT

- calculator

1. **The points A (3, 6) and B (−1, −3) are plotted on a coordinate grid and joined as shown. Work out the exact length of line AB.**

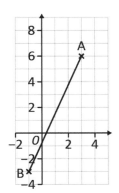

---

2. **The dimensions of three triangles are given below. Which are right-angled? Explain to your tutor how you know.**

   a)   AB = 7 cm, BC = 25 cm, AC = 24 cm   ....

   b)   AB = 0.3 m, BC = 0.2 m, AC = 0.4 m   ....

   c)   AB = 17 cm, BC = 15 cm, AC = 8 cm   ....

3. **The diagonal of a square is 10 cm. What are the exact lengths of the sides of the square?**

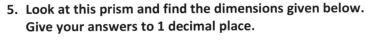

4. **Calculate the area of an isosceles triangle with two sides of length 6 cm and one side of length 5 cm. Give your answer to 2 decimal places.**

---

5. **Look at this prism and find the dimensions given below. Give your answers to 1 decimal place.**

   a)   Calculate its surface area.

   ....

   b)   Calculate the length of the diagonal that joins the mid-point of AB with F.

   ....

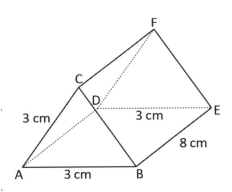

HOMEWORK ACTIVITY: EXPLAIN HOW...   TIMING: **60** MINS

LEARNING OBJECTIVES

- Know the formula for Pythagoras' theorem and apply it to find lengths and angles in right-angled triangles in 2-D and 3-D shapes

EQUIPMENT

- large sheet of paper or video recording device such as a smartphone or tablet

1. Create a poster, flow chart, page of a textbook or video to explain how to:

a) identify a right-angled triangle from the length of the sides

b) find the length of the hypotenuse in a right-angled triangle, given the length of the two shorter sides

c) find the length of one of the shorter sides in a right-angled triangle, given the length of one shorter side and the hypotenuse

d) find the area of an isosceles triangle given the length of the sides

e) find the area of an equilateral triangle given the lengths of the sides

f) find the length of the diagonal of a rectangle

g) find the length of the diagonal of a cuboid.

Make sure you use diagrams and examples so that you can use your explanations for revision.

27 ANSWERS

STARTER ACTIVITY: TRIANGLE CONSTRUCTION

1. a)–c) Check student's drawings.

2. All triangles are right-angled triangles.

3. Triangles a) and c) are similar as their corresponding sides are in the same ratio.

MAIN ACTIVITY: INTRODUCING PYTHAGORAS' THEOREM

1. a) $a^2 + b^2 = c^2$

b) c

2. a)–d) Check the student's drawings.

3. a) $\sqrt{149}$ cm

b) $2\sqrt{149}$ mm

c) $6\sqrt{2}$ cm

4. a) $5\sqrt{2}$

b) $5\sqrt{3}$

MAIN ACTIVITY: APPLYING PYTHAGORAS' THEOREM

1. $\sqrt{97}$

2. a) and c) are right-angled – the sum of the squares of the shorter sides is equal to the square of the longer side.

3. $5\sqrt{2}$

4. 13.64 cm^2

5. a) 79.8 cm^2

b) 8.4 cm

HOMEWORK ACTIVITY: EXPLAIN HOW...

1. Check the student's explanations.

28 GEOMETRY AND MEASURES: USING TRIGONOMETRY

LEARNING OBJECTIVES

- Know and use the formulae for the trigonometry ratios, and apply them to find angles and lengths in right-angled triangles in 2-D and 3-D figures

SPECIFICATION LINKS

- G1, G20

STARTER ACTIVITY

- **Rearranging an equation; 5 minutes; page 180**
  This activity is a precursor to rearranging the trigonometric ratios. Encourage the student to think about the triangle that relates the three values in the equation. If necessary, write the equation using a formula triangle.

MAIN ACTIVITIES

- **Calculating missing lengths; 20 minutes; page 181**
  Model how to find missing lengths in a right-angled triangle using trigonometry. You may wish to invent a mnemonic to help the student remember SOHCAHTOA, such as Studying On Holiday Can Always Have Two Obvious Advantages. When completing question 2, introduce the student to the terms 'angle of elevation' and 'angle of depression'.
- **Calculating missing angles; 20 minutes; page 182**
  Model how to find missing angles in a right-angled triangle. Emphasise that the system is very similar to finding the lengths of sides.

PLENARY ACTIVITY

- **Flow charts; 5 minutes**
  Ask the student to design a flow chart to show how to calculate:
  a) a missing side in a right-angled triangle
  b) a missing angle in a right-angled triangle.

HOMEWORK ACTIVITY

- **Using trigonometry to solve problems; 30 minutes; page 183**
  Full instructions are given on the activity sheet.

SUPPORT IDEA

- **Calculating missing lengths** If the student can identify which trigonometric ratio to use, but struggles to rearrange it, it might help to display SOHCAHTOA in three formula triangles like this:

  O   A   O
  S   H   C   H   T   A

  They can then cover the side they wish to calculate in the relevant triangle and see what calculation they need to do.

EXTENSION IDEA

- **Calculating missing lengths; Calculating missing angles** Sketch a cuboid and challenge the student to find the lengths of sides, diagonals and angles, given set values of side lengths or angles.

PROGRESS AND OBSERVATIONS

Starter activity: Rearranging an equation

Timing: 5 mins

Learning objectives

- Rearrange a simple equation to make a given variable the subject

Equipment

We know that $4 = \dfrac{12}{3}$.

This equation can be rearranged to give: $4 \times 3 = 12$ or $3 = \dfrac{12}{4}$.

1. Use this method to make x the subject of each of these equations.

a) $a = \dfrac{x}{b}$

- -

b) $a = \dfrac{b}{x}$

- -

MAIN ACTIVITY: CALCULATING MISSING LENGTHS TIMING: 20 MINS

LEARNING OBJECTIVES

- Know and use the formulae for the trigonometric ratios, and apply them to find lengths in right-angled triangles in 2-D and 3-D figures

EQUIPMENT

- scientific calculator
- ruler
- protractor

 1. **Draw any right-angled triangle in the space below. Measure one angle and one side and mark them on the triangle. Use trigonometry to calculate the length of the other two sides. Repeat.**

 2. **A man is watching a bird in a tree. The angle of elevation from the horizontal is 35°. He is watching the bird from the ground 12 m horizontally from the bottom of the tree.**

How far up the tree is the bird?
Give your answer to the nearest 10 cm.

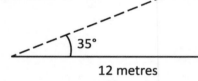

12 metres

Remember, angle of elevation means looking up, and angle of depression means looking down.

 3. **In the cuboid shown, AB = 3 cm and BC = 5 cm. Given that the line AG makes an angle of 50° with the horizontal, calculate the height of the cuboid.**

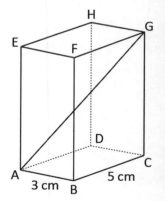

MAIN ACTIVITY: CALCULATING MISSING ANGLES

TIMING: 20 MINS

LEARNING OBJECTIVES

- Know and use the formulae for the trigonometric ratios, and apply them to find angles in right-angled triangles in 2-D and 3-D figures

EQUIPMENT

- scientific calculator
- protractor

1. Draw any right-angled triangle. Measure the length of the sides and mark them on the triangle. Use trigonometry to calculate the size of one (non-right-angled) angle. Check your answer by measuring the angle. Repeat, using different pairs of sides to calculate the angles.

2. A helicopter is hovering, waiting to land. It is 20 feet above ground level and 100 feet horizontally from the landing point.

   Calculate the angle of depression from the helicopter to the landing point.

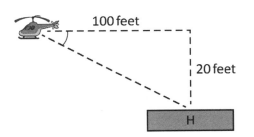

3. A cube has sides of length 6 cm.
   Work out the angle between the base of the cube and the diagonal (*d*).

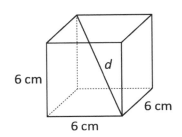

HOMEWORK ACTIVITY: USING TRIGONOMETRY TO SOLVE PROBLEMS   TIMING: 30 MINS

LEARNING OBJECTIVES
- Know and use the formulae for the trigonometric ratios and apply them to find angles and lengths in right-angled triangles in 2-D figures

EQUIPMENT
- scientific calculator

Give your answers to these questions to 1 decimal place.

 1. A ramp is 2 m long. The step is 50 cm high. Work out the angle that the ramp is to the horizontal.

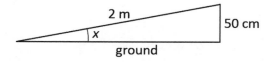

2 m

50 cm

x

ground

 2. A roof is designed so that the angle of the slope with the horizontal is 45°. Work out the lengths of the sloping sides of the roof.

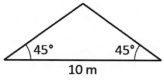

$45°$ $45°$

10 m

 3. Prove that the area of an equilateral triangle with sides of length 1 cm is $\frac{\sqrt{3}}{4}$.

 4. A tent is the shape of a triangular prism. The base measures 1.5 m by 2.5 m, and the sloping height measures 2 m.

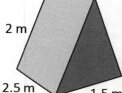

2 m

 a) Calculate the area of fabric used to make the tent. Give your answer to the nearest 0.1 m². The base of the tent is made from the same fabric as the sides.

2.5 m 1.5 m

 b) Calculate the angle that the sloping sides make with the ground. Give your answer to the nearest degree.

28 ANSWERS

STARTER ACTIVITY: REARRANGING AN EQUATION

1. a) $a \times b = x$

b) $x = \dfrac{b}{a}$

MAIN ACTIVITY: CALCULATING MISSING LENGTHS

1. Check the student's drawings.
2. 8.4 m
3. 6.9 cm

MAIN ACTIVITY: CALCULATING MISSING ANGLES

1. Check the student's drawings.
2. 11.3°
3. 35.3°

HOMEWORK ACTIVITY: USING TRIGONOMETRY TO SOLVE PROBLEMS

1. 14.5°
2. both sides = 7.07 m
3. Check the student's proof.
4. a) 16.5 m^2
b) 68°

GLOSSARY

Angle of elevation
The angle formed between the horizontal and a straight line, which makes an angle above the horizontal

Angle of depression
The angle formed between the horizontal and a straight line, which makes an angle below the horizontal

MATHS
— HIGHER —

29 GEOMETRY AND MEASURES: TRIGONOMETRIC VALUES

LEARNING OBJECTIVES

- Know the exact values of sin θ and cos θ for θ = 0°, 30°, 45°, 60° and 90°
- Know the exact value of tan θ for θ = 0°, 30°, 45° and 60°
- Recognise, sketch and interpret graphs of the trigonometric functions

SPECIFICATION LINKS

- G21, G22, G23, A12

STARTER ACTIVITY

- **Ordering numbers; 5 minutes; page 186**
  Remind the student that an exact value can be given by leaving the number in surd form. Encourage the student to estimate the value of each surd (knowing that $\sqrt{1}=1$ and $\sqrt{4}=2$ tells you that $\sqrt{2}$ and $\sqrt{3}$ must be between 1 and 2).

MAIN ACTIVITIES

- **Special triangles and trigonometric graphs; 20 minutes; page 187**
  Look at the special triangles and work through how to find the values of sin, cos and tan of 60°, 30° and 45° using these triangles. Explain to the student that they must learn these values. Look at the graphs of sin x, cos x and tan x and discuss their properties. Read the values of sin and cos for 0° and 90° from the graphs and discuss why tan 90° cannot be found. Use the graphs to find approximate values of the sin/cos/tan of various angles. Discuss the symmetry of the graphs and how this can be used to find other trigonometric values; for example, sin (−45°).

- **Working with non-right-angled triangles; 20 minutes; page 188**
  The student will need to learn the three formulae on this activity sheet. Encourage them to write the formulae on revision cards or photograph them using their phones so they can refer back to them while revising.
  Work through the activity, discussing which formula to use in each circumstance. Ensure that the student always labels the sides and angles (a, b, c and A, B, C respectively) before attempting to use the formulae.

PLENARY ACTIVITY

- **What's my angle?; 5 minutes**
  Sketch two right-angled triangles, one with sides of length 1 cm, 1 cm and $\sqrt{2}$ cm, and one with sides of length 2 cm, 1 cm and $\sqrt{3}$ cm. Invite the student to write the angles of the triangles in the correct places.

HOMEWORK ACTIVITY

- **Trigonometry revision; 60 minutes; page 189**
  Full instructions are given on the activity sheet.

SUPPORT IDEA

- **Working with non-right-angled triangles** Model how to use the sine and cosine rules. Emphasise the importance of correctly labelling the sides. You may also wish to give the student the rearranged cosine rule formula:
  $$\cos A = \frac{b^2 + c^2 - a^2}{2bc}.$$

EXTENSION IDEA

- **Working with non-right-angled triangles** Extend to 3-D shapes, asking the student to use the sine and/or cosine rule to calculate the missing lengths/angles within 3-D shapes.

PROGRESS AND OBSERVATIONS

STARTER ACTIVITY: ORDERING NUMBERS

TIMING: 5 MINS

LEARNING OBJECTIVES

- Order numbers including fractions, decimals and surds

EQUIPMENT

1. **Write these numbers in ascending order.**

$$\frac{1}{2} \qquad \sqrt{2} \qquad 1 \qquad 5^2$$

....

2. **Write these numbers in descending order.**

$$\frac{3}{4} \qquad \sqrt{3} \qquad -1.7 \qquad 4.9$$

....

Edexcel **MATHS** — HIGHER — **TUTORS' GUILD**

MAIN ACTIVITY: SPECIAL TRIANGLES AND TRIGONOMETRIC GRAPHS   TIMING: 20 MINS

LEARNING OBJECTIVES

- Know the exact values of sin θ and cos θ for θ = 0°, 30°, 45°, 60° and 90°
- Know the exact value of tan θ for θ = 0°, 30°, 45° and 60°
- Recognise, sketch and interpret graphs of the trigonometric functions

EQUIPMENT

1. **Look at these graphs and triangles and use the given information to complete the table of trigonometric values.**

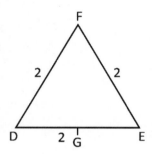

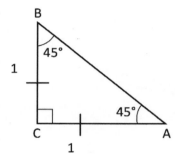

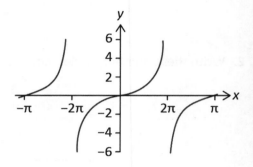

$y = \tan x$

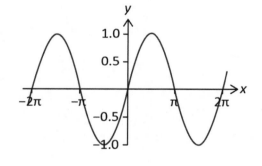

$y = \sin x$

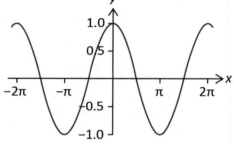

$y = \cos x$

θ	0°	30°	45°	60°	90°
sin θ					
cos θ					
tan θ					

MAIN ACTIVITY: WORKING WITH NON-RIGHT-ANGLED TRIANGLES TIMING: 20 MINS

LEARNING OBJECTIVES

- Know and apply the sine rule and cosine rule
- Know and apply the formula area $= \frac{1}{2}ab\sin C$ to calculate the area or sides of any triangle

EQUIPMENT

- ruler
- protractor
- calculator

1. **Complete each of these formulae.**

   a) Sine rule: $\dfrac{a}{\sin A} = \dfrac{}{\sin B} = \dfrac{c}{}$

   b) Cosine rule: $a^2 = b^2 + \underline{\hspace{1.5cm}} - \underline{\hspace{1.5cm}}$

   c) Area of a triangle: area $= \frac{1}{2} \underline{\hspace{2cm}} \sin C$

2. **Draw a triangle in the space below. Measure and label two of the sides and an included angle.**

   a) Work out the size of all the other sides and angles. Check your answers by measuring them.

   b) Work out the area of the triangle.

3. **Explain when you would use:**

   a) the sine rule

   b) the cosine rule.

4. **If you knew the area of a triangle and two of the side lengths, how could you work out the angles?**

HOMEWORK ACTIVITY: TRIGONOMETRY REVISION   TIMING: 60 MINS

LEARNING OBJECTIVES

- Know the exact values of sin θ and cos θ for θ = 0°, 30°, 45°, 60° and 90°
- Know the exact value of tan θ for θ = 0°, 30°, 45° and 60°
- Recognise, sketch and interpret graphs of the trigonometric functions

EQUIPMENT

- card
- large sheet of paper
- scissors

1. Draw a poster or flow chart showing how to use SOHCAHTOA to find unknown angles and unknown lengths.

2. Cut out these cards and use them to learn the trigonometric values. You could play snap or pairs, display them on the wall, or ask someone to test you.

sin 45°	$\dfrac{1}{\sqrt{2}}$	cos 60°	$\dfrac{1}{2}$
cos 45°	$\dfrac{1}{\sqrt{2}}$	tan 60°	$\sqrt{3}$
tan 45°	1	sin 0°	0
sin 30°	$\dfrac{1}{2}$	cos 0°	1
cos 30°	$\dfrac{\sqrt{3}}{2}$	tan 0°	0
tan 30°	$\dfrac{1}{\sqrt{3}}$	sin 90°	1
sin 60°	$\dfrac{\sqrt{3}}{2}$	cos 90°	0

29 ANSWERS

STARTER ACTIVITY: ORDERING NUMBERS

1. $\frac{1}{2}$ 1 $\sqrt{2}$ 5^2

2. 4.9 $\sqrt{3}$ $\frac{3}{4}$ -1.7

MAIN ACTIVITY: SPECIAL TRIANGLES AND TRIGONOMETRIC GRAPHS

1.

θ	0°	30°	45°	60°	90°
sin θ	0	$\frac{1}{2}$	$\frac{1}{\sqrt{2}}$	$\frac{\sqrt{3}}{2}$	1
cos θ	1	$\frac{\sqrt{3}}{2}$	$\frac{1}{\sqrt{2}}$	$\frac{1}{2}$	0
tan θ	0	$\frac{1}{\sqrt{3}}$	1	$\sqrt{3}$	

MAIN ACTIVITY: WORKING WITH NON-RIGHT-ANGLED TRIANGLES

1. a) Sine rule: $\dfrac{a}{\sin A} = \dfrac{b}{\sin B} = \dfrac{c}{\sin C}$

b) Cosine rule: $a^2 = b^2 + c^2 - 2ac$

c) Area of a triangle: area $= \frac{1}{2}\, ab \sin C$

2. a)–b) Check the student's drawing and calculations.

3. a) When given two sides and an angle opposite one of the sides, or two angles and one side.

b) When given three sides, or two sides and an included angle.

4. Rearrange the area equation to give $\sin C = \dfrac{2 \times \text{area}}{ab}$, then find angle C.

Use the sine or cosine rule to find the second angle.

Find the third angle by subtracting the sum of the first two from 180˚.

HOMEWORK ACTIVITY: TRIGONOMETRY REVISION

1. Check the student's work.

MATHS
— HIGHER —

30 GEOMETRY AND MEASURES: CIRCLES

LEARNING OBJECTIVES	SPECIFICATION LINKS

LEARNING OBJECTIVES

- Identify and apply circle definitions
- Know, prove and use the standard circle theorems
- Calculate arc lengths and angles and areas of circles

SPECIFICATION LINKS

- G9, G10, G17, G18

STARTER ACTIVITY

- **Parts of a circle; 5 minutes; page 192**
  Full instructions are given on the activity sheet.

MAIN ACTIVITIES

- **Circle theorems; 25 minutes; page 193**
  Explain to the student that they must be able to prove each circle theorem. Choose one of the circle theorems and model the proof, explaining that some proofs rely on assumption of another circle theorem.
  Choose one circle theorem and ask the student to prove it, repeating as often as time allows.
- **Arc length and area of a sector; 15 minutes; page 194**
  Ask the student to complete question 1, explaining that they must learn these formulae.
  Model how to find arc length and area of a sector given radius and angle. Draw out from the student how to work backwards to find the angle given area/arc length. Work through questions 2 and 3.

PLENARY ACTIVITY

- **Picture it!; 5 minutes**
  Sketch a diagram illustrating one of the circle theorems or a sector/arc length. Then ask the student to give you all the information they can about the diagram.

HOMEWORK ACTIVITY

- **Circle theorems; 60 minutes; page 195**
  Full instructions are given on the activity sheet.

SUPPORT IDEA

Arc length and area of a sector Add the following additional step to the questions: 2. The area of a sector is 10 cm². The angle in the sector is 60°. Work out the length of the arc.
3. A circle has radius 5 cm. The length of the arc of the circle is 10 cm. a) Work out the angle of the sector; b) Work out the area of the sector.

EXTENSION IDEA

- **Circle theorems** Tell the student that some proofs of the circle theorems assume other circle theorems.
  Ask the student to design an order in which to prove the circle theorems, ensuring that any they use have already been proved.

PROGRESS AND OBSERVATIONS

MATHS
— HIGHER —

STARTER ACTIVITY: PARTS OF A CIRCLE

TIMING: 5 MINS

LEARNING OBJECTIVES

- Identify and apply circle definitions

EQUIPMENT

1. **Label the different parts of the circle using the vocabulary below.**

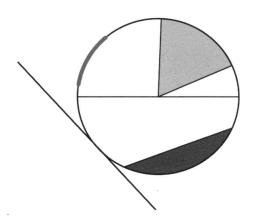

radius   circumference   chord

diameter   tangent   arc

sector   segment

MAIN ACTIVITY: CIRCLE THEOREMS   **TIMING: 25 MINS**

LEARNING OBJECTIVES	EQUIPMENT
• Know, prove and use the standard circle theorems	• plain paper

 1. On a separate sheet of paper, draw diagrams to illustrate these facts.

a) The angle between a tangent and a radius is 90°.

b) The tangents from an external point are equal in length.

 2. Match each of the following diagrams to a circle theorem below. Mark any angles on the diagrams to help to illustrate the theorem.

a)
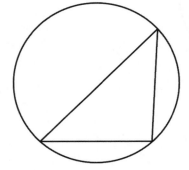

b)
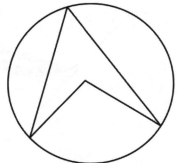

c)
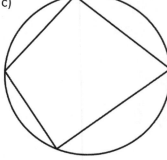

d)
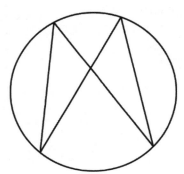

e)
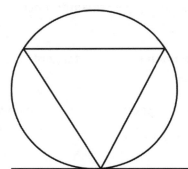

f)
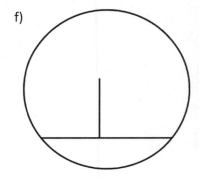

A: The angle subtended by an arc at the centre of a circle is twice the angle subtended at any point on the circumference.

B: The angle in a semicircle is a right angle.

C: The perpendicular from the centre of a circle to a chord bisects the chord.

D: Angles in the same segment are equal.

E: The angle between a chord and a tangent is equal to the angle in the alternate segment.

F: The opposite angles of a cyclic quadrilateral add up to 180°.

MAIN ACTIVITY: ARC LENGTH AND AREA OF A SECTOR   TIMING: 15 MINS

LEARNING OBJECTIVES
- Calculate arc length and angles and areas of circles

EQUIPMENT
- calculator

1. **Write out these formulae. Remember that you need to remember them for your exam!**

    a) arc length = ...

    b) area of a sector = ...

2. **The area of a sector is 10 cm². The angle in the sector is 60°.**
    Work out the length of the arc of the sector. Give your answer in centimetres to 1 decimal place.

    ....

    ....

3. **A circle has radius 5 cm. The length of the arc of the circle is 10 cm. What is the area of the sector?**

    ....

    ....

HOMEWORK ACTIVITY: CIRCLE THEOREMS

TIMING: 60 MINS

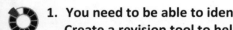

LEARNING OBJECTIVES

- Identify and apply circle definitions
- Know, prove and use the standard circle theorems

EQUIPMENT

- large sheet of paper/index cards/video recording device

1. **You need to be able to identify, prove and use the circle theorems.**
   Create a revision tool to help you to learn the circle theorems.

   You could choose to make a video, a poster, revision cards, a slideshow, a set of exam questions with model answers... It is up to you!

   Make sure you include:

   - **The six circle theorems**

     - The angle subtended by an arc at the centre of a circle is twice the angle subtended at any point on the circumference.

     - The angle in a semicircle is a right angle.

     - The perpendicular from the centre of a circle to a chord bisects the chord.

     - Angles in the same segment are equal.

     - The angle between a chord and a tangent is equal to the angle in the alternate segment.

     - Opposite angles of a cyclic quadrilateral add up to 180°.

   - **The key facts**

     - The angle between a tangent and a radius is 90°.

     - The tangents from an external point are equal in length.

30 ANSWERS

STARTER ACTIVITY: PARTS OF A CIRCLE

1.

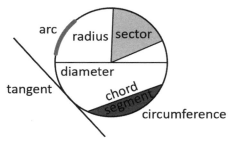

MAIN ACTIVITY: CIRCLE THEOREMS

1. Check student's diagrams.
2. a) B   b) A   c) F   d) D   e) E   f) C

MAIN ACTIVITY: ARC LENGTH AND AREA OF A SECTOR

1. a) arc length $= \dfrac{\theta}{180}\pi r$ b) area of sector $= \dfrac{\theta}{360}\pi r^2$

2. arc length = 4.6 cm

3. area of sector = 25 cm²

HOMEWORK ACTIVITY: CIRCLE THEOREMS

1. Check the student's work. Ask them some questions to check understanding.

GLOSSARY

Radius
A straight line that joins the centre of a circle to any point on the circumference

Diameter
A straight line that joins two points on the circumference of a circle and goes through the centre

Chord
A straight line joining any two points on the circumference of a circle

Circumference
The perimeter of a circle

Arc
Part of the circumference of a circle

Segment
Part of a circle that is bounded by an arc and a chord

Sector
Part of a circle bounded by two radii and an arc

Tangent (to a circle)
A straight line that is perpendicular to the radius at that point on the circumference

31 GEOMETRY AND MEASURES: VECTORS

LEARNING OBJECTIVES

- Apply addition, subtraction and multiplication by a scalar of vectors
- Diagrammatic and column representation of vectors
- Use vectors to construct geometrical arguments and proof
- Transform shapes using rotation, reflection, enlargement and translation

SPECIFICATION LINKS

- G1, G6, G7, G8, G24, G25,

STARTER ACTIVITY

- **Length of line segments; 5 minutes; page 198**
  Full instructions are given on the activity sheet.

MAIN ACTIVITIES

- **Introducing vectors; 25 minutes; page 199**
  Show the student standard vector notation ($\overrightarrow{AB}$ or **a**) and challenge them to write the column vector that describes the movement between different pairs of points. Establish which vectors are equivalent ($\overrightarrow{BA}$ and $\overrightarrow{DC}$, $\overrightarrow{CE}$ and $\overrightarrow{BF}$, $\overrightarrow{HG}$ and $\overrightarrow{IC}$), and extend this to vectors $\overrightarrow{AB}$ and $\overrightarrow{CD}$, $\overrightarrow{EC}$ and $\overrightarrow{FB}$ and $\overrightarrow{GH}$ and $\overrightarrow{CI}$ therefore being equivalent. Explain that parallel vectors are multiples of one another, and that you can show they are parallel by joining the points with straight lines.
- **Vectors and proof; 15 minutes; page 200**
  Spend some time discussing what it means for vectors to be parallel and co-linear. Encourage the student to sketch diagrams to support their understanding of these problems.

PLENARY ACTIVITY

- **Vector facts; 5 minutes**
  Give the student five minutes to write as many facts as they can about vectors and how to solve vector problems.

HOMEWORK ACTIVITY

- **Transformations; 20 minutes; page 201**
  Full instructions are given on the activity sheet.

SUPPORT IDEA

- **Introducing vectors** Support the student by drawing the horizontal and then vertical 'journey' between the points.

EXTENSION IDEA

- **Vectors and proof** Ask the student to find a vector parallel to $\begin{pmatrix} a \\ b \end{pmatrix}$ and to define what it means for three points to be co-linear.

PROGRESS AND OBSERVATIONS

STARTER ACTIVITY: LENGTH OF LINE SEGMENTS   TIMING: 5 MINS

LEARNING OBJECTIVES
- Calculate the length of a line segment

EQUIPMENT
- ruler

1. On the coordinate axis, mark the points A (−2, 5), B (3, −4) and C (−3, −7).

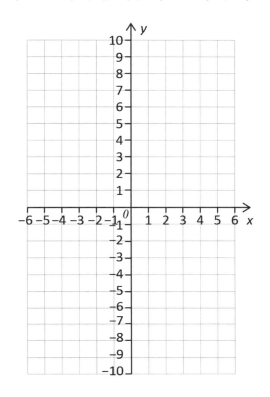

2. Work out the exact length of each of these line segments.

   a) AB   ....

   b) BC   ....

   c) AC   ....

MAIN ACTIVITY: INTRODUCING VECTORS

TIMING: 25 MINS

LEARNING OBJECTIVES

- Apply addition, subtraction and multiplication by a scalar of vectors
- Diagrammatic and column representation of vectors

EQUIPMENT

- ruler

1. Points A to I have been plotted on the coordinate grid opposite.

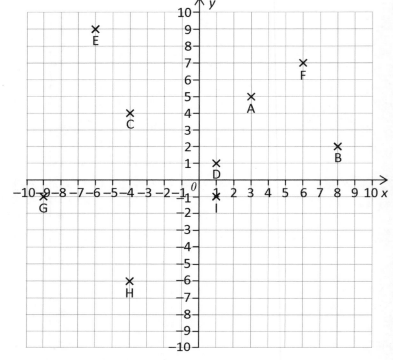

a) $\vec{BJ} = \begin{pmatrix} -1 \\ -2 \end{pmatrix}$. Mark point J on the diagram.

b) Write $\vec{JB}$ as a column vector.

----

c) Which vector on the diagram is parallel to vector $\vec{BJ}$? Explain how you could work this out given just the column vector for each possible pair of points.

----

d) Write three vectors in column vector form that would be parallel to $\vec{AF}$.

----

e) If you knew vector $\vec{XY}$, explain how you could easily write down vector $\vec{YX}$.

----

2. Calculate the magnitude of vector $\vec{JB}$.

----

3. Work out the resultant of $\vec{AB} + \vec{BC}$. Explain why this is equal to $\vec{AC}$.

MAIN ACTIVITY: VECTORS AND PROOF

TIMING: 15 MINS

LEARNING OBJECTIVES

- Use vectors to construct geometrical arguments and proof

EQUIPMENT

1. **Using the vectors below, write each of the following vector calculations as a single column vector.**

$$a = \begin{pmatrix} -2 \\ 5 \end{pmatrix} \qquad b = \begin{pmatrix} 3 \\ 8 \end{pmatrix} \qquad c = \begin{pmatrix} 4 \\ -10 \end{pmatrix} \qquad d = \begin{pmatrix} 0 \\ -7 \end{pmatrix}$$

a) 2**b** ....

b) **b** + **c** ....

c) 5**a** – **d** ....

d) –**a** ....

e) –3**a** + 2**d** ....

2. **Explain how you know that d is parallel to the *y*-axis.**

....

3. **Prove that c is parallel to a.**

....

4. **Look at this vector diagram.**

$\overrightarrow{MO} = a$ $\qquad$ $\overrightarrow{MN} = b$
Q is the mid-point of line MO. OP is two thirds of the length of ON.

Prove that QPR is a straight line.

Hint: First work out $\overrightarrow{QO}$ and $\overrightarrow{ON}$, then work out $\overrightarrow{OP}$ and $\overrightarrow{PN}$. Work out and simplify $\overrightarrow{QP}$ and $\overrightarrow{PR}$, then show that $\overrightarrow{QP}$ is a multiple of $\overrightarrow{PR}$.

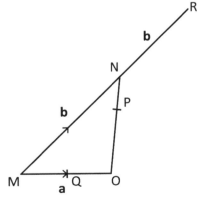

....

....

....

MATHS
— HIGHER —

HOMEWORK ACTIVITY: TRANSFORMATIONS

TIMING: 20 MINS

LEARNING OBJECTIVES

- Describe translations as 2-D vectors
- Describe the changes and invariance achieved by combinations of rotations, reflections and enlargements

EQUIPMENT

- rule

1. **Shape A has been drawn on the coordinate grid below.**

   a) Translate shape A through $\begin{pmatrix} -5 \\ 2 \end{pmatrix}$.

      Label the shape B.

   b) Reflect B in the line $x = -2$. Label the shape C.

   c) Rotate C through 90° about the point (0, 8). Label the shape D.

   d) Reflect D in the line $y = 8$. Label the shape E.

   e) Rotate E 270° about the point (−2, 0). Label the shape F.

   f) Describe the single transformation that will move shape F to shape A.

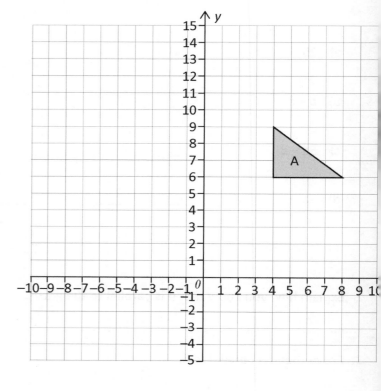

   ....

   g) What can you say about all the triangles on the diagram?

   ....

   h) Write down three vectors parallel to the vector that moved A to B.   ....

2. **Enlarge shape A:**

   a) about (10, 10) with scale factor 2. Label the shape G.

   b) about the point (2, 3) with scale factor $\dfrac{1}{2}$. Label the shape H.

31 ANSWERS

STARTER ACTIVITY: LENGTH OF LINE SEGMENTS

1. Check plotted points.

2. a) $\sqrt{97}$ b) $3\sqrt{5}$ c) $\sqrt{145}$

MAIN ACTIVITY: INTRODUCING VECTORS

1. a) Point J should be at (0, 7).   b) $\begin{pmatrix} 1 \\ 2 \end{pmatrix}$ c) $\overrightarrow{AD}$ since it is a multiple of $\begin{pmatrix} 1 \\ 2 \end{pmatrix}$.

d) Any vectors of the form $\begin{pmatrix} 3a \\ 2a \end{pmatrix}$.   e) Change the signs of both parts of the vector.

2. $\sqrt{5}$ 3. $\begin{pmatrix} -7 \\ -1 \end{pmatrix}$ It is equivalent as it describes the same journey.

MAIN ACTIVITY: VECTORS AND PROOF

1. a) $\begin{pmatrix} 6 \\ 16 \end{pmatrix}$ b) $\begin{pmatrix} 7 \\ -2 \end{pmatrix}$ c) $\begin{pmatrix} -10 \\ 32 \end{pmatrix}$ d) $\begin{pmatrix} 2 \\ -5 \end{pmatrix}$ e) $\begin{pmatrix} 6 \\ -29 \end{pmatrix}$

2. The movement parallel to the x-axis is zero.

3. $\mathbf{c} = -2\mathbf{a}$

4. $\overrightarrow{QO} = \dfrac{1}{2}\mathbf{a}$ and $\overrightarrow{ON} = -\mathbf{a} + \mathbf{b}$ $\overrightarrow{OP} = -\dfrac{2}{3}\mathbf{a} + \dfrac{2}{3}\mathbf{b}$ and $\overrightarrow{PN} = -\dfrac{1}{3}\mathbf{a} + \dfrac{1}{3}\mathbf{b}$; $\overrightarrow{QP} = -\dfrac{1}{6}\mathbf{a} + \dfrac{2}{3}\mathbf{b}$ and $\overrightarrow{PR} = -\dfrac{1}{3}\mathbf{a} + \dfrac{4}{3}\mathbf{b}$

$\overrightarrow{QP} = \dfrac{1}{6}(-\mathbf{a} + 4\mathbf{b})$ and $\overrightarrow{PR} = \dfrac{1}{3}(-\mathbf{a} + 4\mathbf{b})$, therefore $\overrightarrow{QP}$ is a multiple of $\overrightarrow{PR}$.

HOMEWORK ACTIVITY: TRANSFORMATIONS

1. a)–e) and 2. a)–b) See diagram.

1. f) Translate F through vector $\begin{pmatrix} 11 \\ 4 \end{pmatrix}$

g) They are all congruent.

h) Any vectors of the form $\begin{pmatrix} -5a \\ 2a \end{pmatrix}$

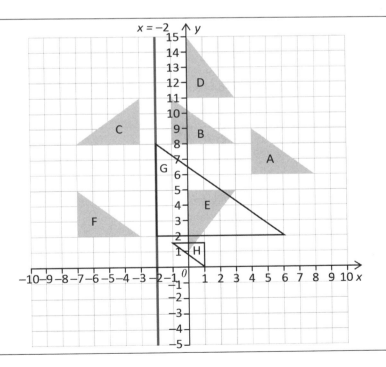

GLOSSARY

Vector
The displacement from one position to another; can be pictured geometrically as a line segment; has magnitude and direction

Co-linear
Points lying on the same straight line

32 PROBABILITY: BASIC PROBABILITY AND VENN DIAGRAMS

LEARNING OBJECTIVES

- Mark events on a probability scale
- Calculate probability from a frequency table
- Compare experimental data and theoretical probabilities
- Calculate missing probabilities
- Understand and use mutually exclusive events
- Find the probability of an event not occurring
- Work out probabilities from Venn diagrams

SPECIFICATION LINKS

- N1, P1, P2, P3, P4, P5, P6

STARTER ACTIVITY

- **Ordering; 5 minutes; page 204**
  Before completing the activity, remind the student how to convert between fractions, decimals and percentages.

MAIN ACTIVITIES

- **Colouring in; 25 minutes; page 205**
  Explain to the student that each grid must be coloured in to satisfy the statement underneath. Encourage the student to recognise that there is often more than one way in which to do this, and to explain what parameters they need to meet for each grid.

- **Venn diagrams; 15 minutes; page 206**
  Discuss with the student what a Venn diagram is, and introduce the notation by working through the information on the activity sheet. Explain that Venn diagrams can be used to help with probability calculations. Then ask the student to complete question 2 on the activity sheet.

PLENARY ACTIVITY

- **Rolling a dice; 5 minutes**
  Ask the student to roll a dice 10 times and tally the results. Establish the experimental probability of rolling different values and discuss whether this is equal to the theoretical probability. Roll the dice another 20 times and compare experimental probability with theoretical probability again. Establish that the more times the dice is rolled, the closer the experimental probability should become to the theoretical probability.

HOMEWORK ACTIVITY

- **Time to practise; 15 minutes; page 207**
  Full instructions are given on the activity sheet.

SUPPORT IDEA

- **Venn diagrams** Draw a Venn diagram with two overlapping sectors labelled A and B. Ask the student to shade the areas that represent A, B, A∩B, A∪B, A' and B'.

EXTENSION IDEA

- **Colouring in** Challenge the student to find as many different ways as they can to satisfy the criteria for each question on the grid. Which ones have an infinite number of options?

PROGRESS AND OBSERVATIONS

STARTER ACTIVITY: ORDERING

TIMING: 5 MINS

LEARNING OBJECTIVES	EQUIPMENT
• Order positive integers, decimals and fractions	none

1. **Write these numbers in ascending order.**

0.6 $\frac{2}{3}$ 65%   0.608 $\frac{32}{50}$ 68%

....

Edexcel

MATHS

— HIGHER —

MAIN ACTIVITY: COLOURING IN

TIMING: 25 MINS

LEARNING OBJECTIVES

- Calculate probability from frequency tables
- Compare experimental data and theoretical probabilities
- Calculate missing probabilities
- Understand and use mutually exclusive events
- Find the probability of an event not occurring

EQUIPMENT

- coloured pencils

1. **A square is picked at random from each grid. Colour each grid to satisfy the restrictions given.**

The probability of not picking a blue square is $\frac{1}{4}$.

The squares are blue, red or green. The probability of picking a blue square is three times that of picking a green square.

The probability of picking a blue square is 0.1, a red square is 0.5 and a yellow square is 0.3.

A square is randomly chosen and the colour noted in a tally chart.

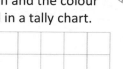

Colour	Tally
Pink	//
Orange	////
Blue	///

The probability of picking different colour squares is shown in the table below.

Colour	blue	red	yellow
Probability	$\frac{1}{2}$	$\frac{1}{5}$	$\frac{3}{10}$

A square is randomly chosen 100 times.
50 times it was red, 12 times it was green and 38 times it was blue.

In a test of 50 random selections, the number of blue squares picked was 27.

The probability of picking different colour squares is shown in the table below.

Colour	blue	red	yellow
Probability	$x + 0.1$	$2x - 0.8$	0.2

$P(\text{not green}) = \frac{4}{5}$ and $P(\text{red or blue}) = \frac{7}{10}$.

2. **Adrian picks a square 5 times and picks 3 greens and 2 blues. Brian picks a square 20 times and picks 10 greens and 10 blues. There are 10 squares. How could you shade the squares? Justify your answer.**

MATHS
— HIGHER —

Edexcel

MAIN ACTIVITY: VENN DIAGRAMS

TIMING: 15 MINS

LEARNING OBJECTIVES

- Work out probabilities from Venn diagrams

EQUIPMENT

A set of values is a group of numbers. You can show the members of a set by listing them inside curly brackets.

If X is the set of even numbers smaller than 10 we can write this as: X = {2, 4, 6, 8}

If Y is the set of prime numbers smaller than 10 we can write this as: Y = {2, 3, 5, 7}

Learn these symbols:

Symbol	Meaning	Example
$\in$	belongs to	2 is in the set X so we can say 2 $\in$ X
X'	not X	X' is all the numbers being considered that are not in the set X X' = {1, 3, 5, 7, 9}
$\cup$	union (or)	X $\cup$ Y is all the elements in set X **or** in set Y X $\cup$ Y = {2, 3, 4, 5, 6, 7, 8}
$\cap$	intersect (and)	X $\cap$ Y is all the elements in set X **and** in set Y X $\cap$ Y = {2}
ξ	the universal set (all elements being considered)	ξ = positive whole numbers smaller than 10

1. **Complete this Venn diagram for sets X and Y as described above.**

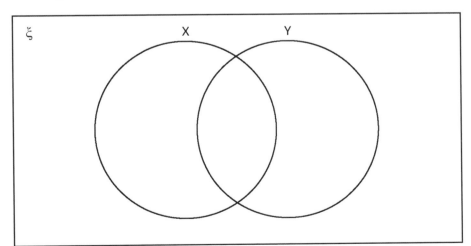

2. **A positive integer less than 10 is chosen at random. Work out these probabilities.**

a) P(X)   ....

b) P(Y')   ....

c) P(X $\cap$ Y)   ....

d) P(X $\cup$ Y)   ....

e) P (X $\cap$ Y') ....

HOMEWORK ACTIVITY: TIME TO PRACTISE   TIMING: 15 MINS

LEARNING OBJECTIVES	EQUIPMENT
	none

- Calculate probability from frequency tables
- Compare experimental data and theoretical probabilities
  Calculate missing probabilities
- Understand and use mutually exclusive events
- Find the probability of an event not occurring

1. In a bag of sweets, there are four different colours. There are 20 red sweets, 12 blue sweets, 7 green sweets and 1 yellow sweet. April takes a sweet at random.

a) Write down the probability that she takes a green sweet. ....

b) Write down the probability that she takes a yellow or blue sweet. ....

c) She takes a green sweet and eats it. She then takes another sweet. ....
   What is the probability that the second sweet is red?

A dice showing the numbers 1–6 is rolled. The dice is biased. The probability of rolling each number is given in the table below.

Number	1	2	3	4	5	6
Probability	x	$3x$	$5x - 0.1$	$10x$	$x + 0.1$	$x - 0.05$

2. The dice is rolled 200 times. How many times would you expect to roll a 5?

....

3. Here is a Venn diagram of sets A, B and ξ.

a) Write down the numbers that are in these sets.

   i) A ∪ B   ....

   ii) B′   ....

b) A number is chosen at random from the diagram. What is the probability that the number is in set A ∩ B?

....

ξ

A   B   6

3   8

2

4   1   0

7

5   9

10

32 ANSWERS

STARTER ACTIVITY: ORDERING

1. 0.6   0.608 $\dfrac{32}{50}$ 65% $\dfrac{2}{3}$ 68%

MAIN ACTIVITY: COLOURING IN

1.

15 squares blue, 5 other colour(s)	blue and green squares in the ratio 3 : 1	1 blue, 5 red, 3 yellow, 1 another colour
4 pink, 10 orange, 6 blue	10 blue, 4 red, 6 yellow	5 red, 1 green, 4 blue
5 blue, the rest another colour	6 blue, 2 red, 2 yellow	2 green, 7 blue OR red, 1 any other colour

2. Various answers are acceptable but the student should recognise that the larger the number of trials, the more likely it is that the relative frequency will equal the theoretical probability.

MAIN ACTIVITY: VENN DIAGRAMS

1.

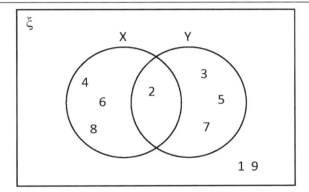

2. a) $\dfrac{4}{9}$ b) $\dfrac{5}{9}$ c) $\dfrac{1}{9}$ d) $\dfrac{7}{9}$ e) $\dfrac{3}{9} = \dfrac{1}{3}$

HOMEWORK ACTIVITY: TIME TO PRACTISE

1. a) $\dfrac{7}{40}$ b) $\dfrac{13}{40}$ c) $\dfrac{20}{39}$

2. 30

3. a) i) 1, 2, 3, 4, 5, 7, 8, 9   ii) 0, 3, 4, 5, 6, 10

b) $\dfrac{2}{11}$

33 PROBABILITY: COMBINED PROBABILITY

LEARNING OBJECTIVES

- Construct theoretical possibility spaces for single and combined experiments with equally likely outcomes, and use these to calculate theoretical probabilities
- Apply systematic listing strategies

SPECIFICATION LINKS

- P7, P8, N5

STARTER ACTIVITY

- **T-shirt factory; 10 minutes; page 210**
  Encourage the student to list the outcomes in question 1 systematically to ensure that they include all possible outcomes. For question 2, guide the student towards multiplying the number of different sizes by the number of different emojis.

MAIN ACTIVITIES

- **More than one event; 20 minutes; page 211**
  Explain to the student that they will be thinking about more than one event occurring. Discuss how this could be represented. Establish that a sample space or Venn diagram is useful if the events occur concurrently, and a tree diagram is useful if the events occur consecutively. You may need to explain or remind the student about the meanings of 'concurrent' and 'consecutive'. Ask the student to work through the questions on the activity sheet.

- **Tree diagrams; 20 minutes; page 212**
  Discuss with the student what a tree diagram looks like and demonstrate how to construct a tree diagram. Explain that the number of 'branches' is equal to the number of possible outcomes. Reinforce that the sum of the probabilities on each column should be 1. Work through the activity sheet, stressing the difference between the two situations with or without replacement. You may wish to draw new tree diagrams for questions 2 and 3 for extra practice.

PLENARY ACTIVITY

- **A fair game; 5 minutes**
  Explain to the student that you are going to play a game with dice. Produce two dice and say that you will roll the dice and add together the values. If the outcome is greater than 6, you win; if it is less than 6, the student wins. Play a few rounds and ask the student to decide if this game is fair or not. Ask them to explain why they think it is unfair.

HOMEWORK ACTIVITY

- **A fair game; 30 minutes; page 213**
  This activity depends on the plenary, so ensure that the student does not miss doing the plenary. Full instructions are given on the activity sheet.

SUPPORT IDEA

- **Tree diagrams** Model the problem using marbles or coloured pencils to help the student to visualise the problem. You could use coloured sweets and eat the first one.

EXTENSION IDEA

- **More than one event** Ask the student to draw up their own two-way table for a game in which two events occur (2 dice rolled, 1 dice 1 coin, 1 dice 1 card). Ask them to design one game that is fair for both players, and one that is biased in their favour.

PROGRESS AND OBSERVATIONS

STARTER ACTIVITY: T-SHIRT FACTORY

TIMING: 10 MINS

LEARNING OBJECTIVES

- Apply systematic listing strategies

EQUIPMENT

1. **A factory produces T-shirts in three sizes: small, medium and large.**
   They use two logos on the T-shirts: smiley emoji and thumbs-up emoji.

   How many different T-shirts are made? List them all.

   ----

2. **The factory decides to introduce a third type of emoji logo: laughing face.**
   How many different T-shirts are there now? How could you work it out without listing them all?

MAIN ACTIVITY: MORE THAN ONE EVENT
TIMING: 20 MINS

LEARNING OBJECTIVES

- Construct theoretical possibility spaces for single and combined experiments with equally likely outcomes and use these to calculate theoretical probabilities
- Calculate the probability of independent and dependent combined events

EQUIPMENT

 1. A factory employs 50 people: 35 women and 15 men. 17 women and 8 men drive to work and the others walk. Complete this two-way table showing this information.

	Women	Men	Total
Drive			
Walk			
Total			

 2. A worker is chosen at random. What is the probability that the worker:

a) drives to work? ....

b) is female and walks to work? ....

c) is male and walks to work? ....

 3. A driver is chosen at random. What is the probability that the driver is:

a) male? ....

b) female? ....

4. At a music school, 41 students play a string instrument, 38 play a brass instrument and 38 play a wind instrument.

Of these, 12 students play all three types of instrument, 4 play only wind instruments, 3 play only brass instruments and 14 play only string instruments.

Given that 7 students play string and wind but not brass, complete the Venn diagram and then work out the probability that a student, chosen at random, plays exactly two types of instrument.

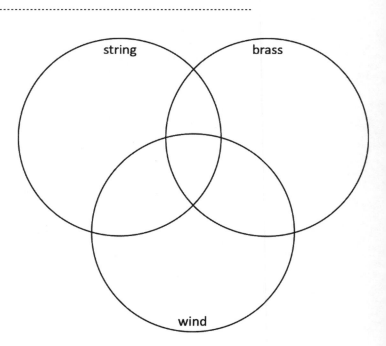

MAIN ACTIVITY: TREE DIAGRAMS

TIMING: 20 MINS

LEARNING OBJECTIVES	EQUIPMENT

- Construct theoretical possibility spaces for single and combined experiments with equally likely outcomes and use these to calculate theoretical probabilities
- Calculate the probability of independent and dependent combined events

1. **A box of chocolate contains 3 hard centres and 7 soft centres. Erica takes a chocolate, eats it and then takes another.**

    a) Complete the tree diagram showing the probabilities and possible outcomes.

    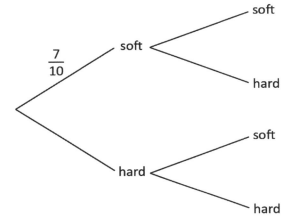

    b) Use your tree diagram to work out the probability of Erica taking:

    i) two soft centres   ....

    ii) one of each type   ....

    iii) at least one soft centre.   ....

    c) If Erica had put the first chocolate back, would the tree be different? If so, explain how.

    ----

    d) Work out the answers to part b) if Erica had returned the chocolate to the box.

    ----

    e) Erica takes and eats three chocolates, one at a time.
        What is the probability that they are all soft centred?

MATHS
— HIGHER —

HOMEWORK ACTIVITY: A FAIR GAME

TIMING: 30 MINS

LEARNING OBJECTIVES

- Calculate the probability of independent and dependent combined events

EQUIPMENT

At the end of the lesson, you played a game where you rolled two dice and added them to work out the score. If the score was greater than 6, your tutor won, if it was less than 6, you won.
Think about whether that game was fair.

1. **In another game, the rules are to find the product of the two numbers on the dice.**

   a) Complete the sample space below to show all the possible outcomes.

		Dice 1					
		1	2	3	4	5	6
Dice 2	1	1	2	3			
	2						
	3						
	4						
	5						
	6						

   b) Decide on rules that would make this game fair.

   ....

   ....

2. **Design a fairground game involving two dice. Decide how much the game will cost, what will create a 'win' and what the monetary prize will be.**

   Think about:

   - how you can make the game interesting enough so that people will play it

   - how you can make money from people playing the game!

   ....

   ....

   ....

   ....

   ....

   ....

33 ANSWERS

STARTER ACTIVITY: T-SHIRT FACTORY

1. 6 T-shirts: smiley + small; smiley + medium; smiley + large; thumbs up + small; thumbs up + medium; thumbs up + large
2. 9. Multiply 3 by 3.

MAIN ACTIVITY: MORE THAN ONE EVENT

1.

	Women	Men	Total
Drive	17	8	25
Walk	18	7	25
Total	35	15	50

2. a) $\frac{1}{2}$ b) $\frac{9}{25}$ c) $\frac{7}{50}$

3. a) $\frac{8}{25}$ b) $\frac{17}{25}$

4. See diagram. Probability is $\frac{30}{63}$.

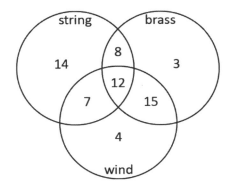

MAIN ACTIVITY: TREE DIAGRAMS

1. a) See diagram.

b) i) $\frac{7}{15}$ ii) $\frac{7}{15}$ iii) $\frac{14}{15}$

c) Yes, the denominator on the second column would be 10 and the numerators would stay the same.

d) i) $\frac{49}{100}$ ii) $\frac{21}{50}$ iii) $\frac{91}{100}$

e) $\frac{7}{24}$

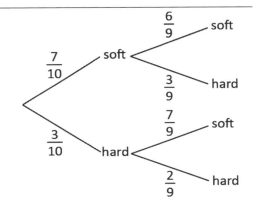

HOMEWORK ACTIVITY: A FAIR GAME

1. a)

		Dice 1					
		1	2	3	4	5	6
Dice 2	1	1	2	3	4	5	6
	2	2	4	6	8	10	12
	3	3	6	9	12	15	18
	4	4	8	12	16	20	24
	5	5	10	15	20	25	30
	6	6	12	18	24	30	36

b) Any game that splits the values so that there are 18 ways of each player winning.
2. Check the student's work.

34 PROBABILITY: CONDITIONAL PROBABILITY

LEARNING OBJECTIVES	SPECIFICATION LINKS
• Calculate and interpret conditional probabilities	• P4, P6, P8, P9

STARTER ACTIVITY

- **How many sweets?; 5 minutes; page 216**
  Full instructions are given on the activity sheet.

MAIN ACTIVITIES

- **More Venn diagrams; 15 minutes; page 217**
  With the student, read the information on the activity sheet and work through drawing a Venn diagram to help them. Look at questions a) and b) and discuss with the student the difference between them. Encourage the student to explain in their own words what the difference is.
- **More tree diagrams; 25 minutes; page 218**
  Draw the student's attention to the fact that for the tree diagrams in the left-hand column, the ball is replaced, while for the tree diagrams in the right-hand column, the ball is not replaced. Encourage the student to voice any thoughts and questions. Also encourage the student to recognise that in all the instances, the events 'picking a red ball' and 'picking a green ball' are mutually exclusive, so the probabilities must add up to 1. After completing the tree diagrams, challenge the student to give you the probability of taking a green ball given that a red ball has already been drawn.

PLENARY ACTIVITY

- **Algebraic tree diagrams; 5 minutes**
  Given that there are x balls in a bag, of which y are red and the rest are blue, draw a tree diagram showing the possible outcomes if two balls are taken from the bag. Do this twice, once with replacement and once without replacement.

HOMEWORK ACTIVITY

- **Exam-style questions; 20 minutes; page 219**
  Full instructions are given on the activity sheet.

SUPPORT IDEA

- **More tree diagrams** Ask the student to look at the left-hand column. Discuss what they know about the sum of the probabilities on each pair of branches. Challenge the student to work out the missing 'pair' first, before moving on to the other branches.

EXTENSION IDEA

- **More tree diagrams** Challenge the student to explain why you need to know the number of balls in the bag for the questions in the right-hand column. You may wish to remove this piece of information for one of the tree diagrams and ask the student to find more than one solution.

PROGRESS AND OBSERVATIONS

STARTER ACTIVITY: HOW MANY SWEETS?

TIMING: 5 MINS

LEARNING OBJECTIVES

* Solve problems involving probability

EQUIPMENT

1. **In a bag of toffees, there are three different flavours. The probability of picking each flavour is given below:**

   mint: $\frac{1}{2}$ chocolate: $\frac{2}{5}$ black treacle: $\frac{1}{10}$

   What would be the smallest number of toffees in the bag for this to be true?
   Explain how you worked out your answer.

MAIN ACTIVITY: MORE VENN DIAGRAMS   **TIMING: 15 MINS**

LEARNING OBJECTIVES

- Calculate the probability of independent and dependent events using tree diagrams
- Calculate and interpret conditional probabilities

EQUIPMENT

 1. 200 cars took an MOT. Of these, 150 passed the test and 50 failed.

Of the 50 that failed, there were only three different faults: 22 had an electrical fault, 22 had cracked windscreens, and 25 had brake failure. No car had all three faults.

15 cars had only an electrical fault, 3 had only cracked windscreens and 12 had both brake failure and a cracked windscreen.

A car is chosen at random.

a) What is the probability that the car's only fault is brake failure?

----

b) Given that the car had brake failure, what is the probability that it had no other faults?

----

c) Explain why your answers to these questions are not the same.

MATHS
— HIGHER —

Edexcel

MAIN ACTIVITY: MORE TREE DIAGRAMS

TIMING: 25 MINS

LEARNING OBJECTIVES

- Calculate the probability of independent and dependent events using tree diagrams
- Calculate and interpret conditional probabilities

EQUIPMENT

1. **Each of these tree diagrams shows the probability of choosing two balls from a bag containing only red and green balls. Use the information given for each situation to complete the tree diagrams.**

The first ball is replaced before the second ball is taken out.	The first ball is NOT replaced before the second ball is taken.

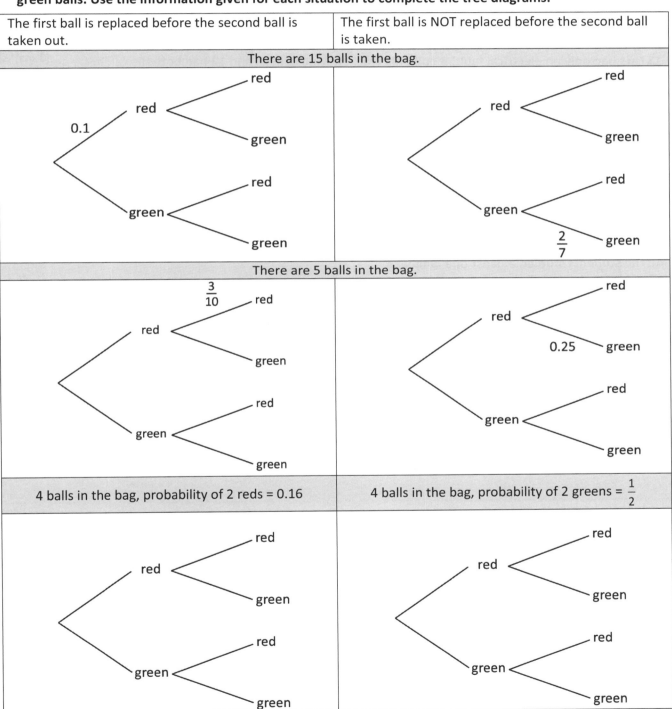

MATHS
— HIGHER —

| HOMEWORK ACTIVITY: EXAM-STYLE QUESTIONS | TIMING: 20 MINS |

LEARNING OBJECTIVES
- Calculate and interpret conditional probabilities

EQUIPMENT
- calculator

1. **A biased dice is rolled twice. Given that the probability of rolling two prime numbers is 0.09, work out the probability of rolling exactly one prime number in both rolls of the dice.**

(3 marks)

2. **60% of people surveyed one morning had used public transport. If two people were chosen at random from the survey, the probability they would both have used public transport would be $\frac{23}{65}$. How many people were surveyed?**

(4 marks)

3. **A survey was done of 100 foreign language students. They studied French, Spanish and German.**
   All the students studied at least one language.
   17 students studied all three languages.
   Altogether, 60 studied French.
   18 studied only German.
   3 studied German and Spanish but not French.
   18 studied French and Spanish but not German.
   43 studied more than one language.

   A student is chosen at random.

   a) Work out the probability that this student studied only Spanish.

(4 marks)

   b) Given that the student studied French, work out the probability that they also studied Spanish.

(2 marks)

219

34 ANSWERS

STARTER ACTIVITY: HOW MANY SWEETS?

1. 20, since this is the LCM of 10, 5 and 2.

MAIN ACTIVITY: MORE VENN DIAGRAMS

1. a) $\frac{13}{200}$ b) $\frac{13}{25}$ c) Part b) is conditional, since the vehicle is chosen from those that have brake failure.

MAIN ACTIVITY: MORE TREE DIAGRAMS

1.

The first ball is replaced before the second ball is taken out.	The first ball is NOT replaced before the second ball is taken.

First tree (replaced):
- 0.1 → red
  - 0.1 → red
  - 0.9 → green
- 0.9 → green
  - 0.1 → red
  - 0.9 → green

Second tree (not replaced):
- $\frac{2}{3}$ → red
  - $\frac{9}{14}$ → red
  - $\frac{5}{14}$ → green
- $\frac{1}{3}$ → green
  - $\frac{5}{7}$ → red
  - $\frac{2}{7}$ → green

Third tree (replaced):
- $\frac{3}{10}$ → red
  - $\frac{3}{10}$ → red
  - $\frac{7}{10}$ → green
- $\frac{7}{10}$ → green
  - $\frac{3}{10}$ → red
  - $\frac{7}{10}$ → green

Fourth tree (not replaced):
- 0.8 → red
  - 0.75 → red
  - 0.25 → green
- 0.2 → green
  - 1 → red
  - 0 → green

Fifth tree (replaced):
- 0.04 → red
  - 0.04 → red
  - 0.96 → green
- 0.96 → green
  - 0.04 → red
  - 0.96 → green

Sixth tree (not replaced):
- $\frac{1}{4}$ → red
  - 0 → red
  - 1 → green
- $\frac{3}{4}$ → green
  - $\frac{1}{3}$ → red
  - $\frac{2}{3}$ → green

HOMEWORK ACTIVITY: EXAM-STYLE QUESTIONS

1. 0.42   2. 40   3. a) $\frac{19}{100}$ b) $\frac{35}{60} = \frac{7}{12}$

35 STATISTICS: PLANNING AN INVESTIGATION AND DATA COLLECTION

LEARNING OBJECTIVES	SPECIFICATION LINKS
• Specify a problem and plan an investigation • Recognise types of data • Understand sampling • Design and use data collection sheets	• A22, S1

STARTER ACTIVITY

• **Which whole numbers; 5 minutes; page 222**
Full instructions are given on the activity sheet. This exercise is designed to familiarise students with using inequalities to represent class widths.

MAIN ACTIVITIES

• **Planning an investigation; 25 minutes; page 223**
Tell the student that they have been asked to find out about reading habits in the UK for a publisher.
Discuss with the student how best to do this. Encourage them to consider all of these points:
  • fairness: all population groups should have an equal chance of being chosen; encourage the student to choose different ages, genders, ethnic backgrounds, social backgrounds and physical locations
  • the type of data they will be collecting (primary/secondary/quantitative/qualitative)
  • how they will ensure a random sample: they could choose people from electoral rolls, conduct a telephone survey, or use stratified sampling
  • size of sample: this should be large enough to be representative of the population, but not so large that the survey becomes too time-consuming and expensive.
When designing the data collection sheet, encourage the student to write questions that are quick and easy to answer. When using or recording grouped data, stress that the groups should not overlap or have gaps between them. They should ideally be of equal width.

• **Stratified sampling; 15 minutes; page 224**
Work through the example with the student. Use the language of proportion and encourage the student to recognise that the proportion of the population is equal to the proportion of the sample.

PLENARY ACTIVITY

• **Limitations of sampling; 5 minutes**
Brainstorm any problems with taking a sample. Discuss the limitations that even a stratified sample has (for example, it is not necessarily a true representation of the population). You may wish to link this to the failure of the polls during the EU referendum.

HOMEWORK ACTIVITY

• **Exam-style questions; 30 minutes; page 225**
Full instructions are given on the activity sheet.

SUPPORT IDEA

• **Planning an investigation** Show the following question to the student:
How many hours a week do you spend reading? 0–1 hours, 1–2 hours or 2–3 hours.
Discuss the problems with these groups (groups overlap and there is no option for more than 3 hours). Ask the student to redesign the question.

EXTENSION IDEA

• **Stratified sampling** Discuss how to tackle a problem if, when calculating the number of people to survey in a stratum, the answer is not a whole number.

PROGRESS AND OBSERVATIONS

STARTER ACTIVITY: WHICH WHOLE NUMBERS?   **TIMING: 5 MINS**

LEARNING OBJECTIVES

- Write whole number values that satisfy inequalities

EQUIPMENT

1. **Write the whole number values that satisfy all of these inequalities:**

   $-3.5 < x \leq 1$

   $0.5 \leq x < \dfrac{7}{4}$

   $-5.2 < x < 7$

MAIN ACTIVITY: PLANNING AN INVESTIGATION

TIMING: 25 MINS

LEARNING OBJECTIVES

- Specify a problem and plan an investigation
- Recognise types of data
- Understand sampling
- Design and use data collection sheets

EQUIPMENT

1. **You are going to carry out an investigation on the reading habits of people in the UK.**

   Discuss how you will carry out this survey, making sure you consider these questions:

   - How can you ensure that you carry out a fair investigation?

   - What type of data will you be recording: primary, secondary, quantitative or qualitative?

   - How large should your sample be and how will you ensure that you get a random sample?

   Design a data collection sheet that you could use to find out about the reading habits of people in the UK.

   Make sure you include some questions to ensure that the data you collect is not biased. For example, you could ask about age, gender and ethnic group.

MAIN ACTIVITY: STRATIFIED SAMPLING

TIMING: 15 MINS

LEARNING OBJECTIVES

- Understand sample and population

EQUIPMENT

Example:

A factory produces batteries in five different sizes.

One day it makes 50 000 batteries.

A sample of 100 batteries will be tested.

How many size A batteries should be tested?

Battery size	Number of batteries produced each day
A	15 000
AA	12 000
AAA	9000
B	7000
C	7000

$$\frac{15\,000}{50\,000} \times 100 = 30 \text{ size A batteries}$$

---

1. **Work out how many of each size of battery should be tested in the example.**

2. **In a school, 255 students are female and 145 are male. A stratified sample of 80 students is being chosen. How many female students should be chosen?**

3. **The population of the UK is around 65 million. Of these, around 7 million people are left-handed. If a survey of 1000 people is taken, write the ratio of left-handed to right-handed people who should be surveyed.**

4. **A company records the methods of transport its staff use to travel to work.**

Transport	% of employees
car	10%
train	72%
bike	2%
walk	16%

The company wishes to survey a sample of 200 people about how far they travel to work.

What type of sampling should you use to ensure that the sample is representative of the population? Explain your answer.

MATHS
— HIGHER —

Edexcel

TUTORS' GUILD

HOMEWORK ACTIVITY: EXAM-STYLE QUESTIONS

TIMING: 30 MINS

LEARNING OBJECTIVES

- Specify a problem and plan an investigation
- Recognise types of data
- Understand sampling
- Design and use data collection sheets

EQUIPMENT

- plain paper

1. **A car manufacturer is researching the most popular colour of car. They decide to record the colour of the next 1000 cars that pass through the factory. What type of data is this? Circle your answer/s.**

   primary   secondary   qualitative   quantitative

   (1 mark)

2. **A tuition company wants to record the number of hits its website has each day. It designs this tally chart.**

Number of hits	Tally
0–1000	
1000–1500	
1500–3000	

   a) Suggest two problems with the tally chart.

   (2 marks)

   b) Re-design the tally chart on a separate sheet of paper.

   (1 mark)

3. **Adrian is carrying out a survey to discover the school's favourite television show. There are 800 students at his school. Explain in detail how he could take:**

   a) a random sample

   (2 marks)

   b) a stratified sample

   (2 marks)

4. **A library has 4500 registered users. Of these, 1300 users are under 18 years of age.**
   The manager carries out a survey of 250 library users. She wants the sample to be representative of the registered users. How many under-18s should be included in the survey?

   (2 marks)

35 ANSWERS

STARTER ACTIVITY: WHICH WHOLE NUMBERS?

1. 1

MAIN ACTIVITY: PLANNING AN INVESTIGATION

1. Check the student's data collection sheet. Check that the questions will ensure that the data collected will be unbiased.

MAIN ACTIVITY: STRATIFIED SAMPLING

1.

Battery size	Number sampled
A	30
AA	24
AAA	18
B	14
C	14

2. 51
3. 27 : 223
4. Stratified sampling, as this will ensure that the number of people surveyed who use each different method of transport will be representative of the overall proportion of the population

HOMEWORK ACTIVITY: EXAM-STYLE QUESTIONS

1. primary and qualitative
2. a) The groups overlap. They have unequal width. There is no category for over 3000 hits.
b)

Number of hits	Tally
$0 \leq h \leq 1000$	
$1000 < h \leq 2000$	
$2000 < h \leq 3000$	
$3000 < h$	

3. a) Take a sample of approximately 80 students – accept any way of randomly selecting students, such as allocating each member of the school a number and randomly generating numbers.
b) Split the school into year and/or gender groups and calculate the proportion in each group. Take a random sample of this proportion of 80 students.
4. 72

GLOSSARY

Primary data
Data collected by you

Secondary data
Data collected by someone else and used by you

Quantitative data
Data that has a numerical value

Qualitative data
Data that is non-numerical

Stratified sample
Contains members of each group in proportion to its fraction of the whole population

36 STATISTICS: CONSTRUCTING GRAPHS, CHARTS AND DIAGRAMS

LEARNING OBJECTIVES

- Draw and read tables, charts and graphs for discrete and categorical data

SPECIFICATION LINKS

- S2

STARTER ACTIVITY

- **3.6 km; 5 minutes; page 228**
  Ask the student to calculate the fractions and percentages of 360 shown on the activity sheet.

MAIN ACTIVITIES

- **Displaying data; 20 minutes; page 229**
  Look at the stem-and-leaf diagram with the student and ensure they understand it by asking questions such as:
  How tall is the tallest/smallest plant? How many plants were at Location A? Then ask the student to complete the back to back stem-and-leaf diagram using the data on the height of seedlings in two locations. When transferring the data into the frequency table, discuss with the students the loss of accuracy of the data, but establish that it makes it simpler to use for charts and diagrams. Then complete the remaining questions.
- **Comparing data; 20 minutes; page 230**
  Look at the two ways in which the data is represented and discuss how to compare the data. Model some calculations, showing the student how to work out how many people each sector represents. Ask the student to work out how many people one sector on the pie chart represents. Work through the 'true/false' questions, encouraging the student to show their calculations as well as explaining in words. Challenge the student to write their own 'true' statements.

PLENARY ACTIVITY

- **Which is best?; 5 minutes**
  Ask the student to choose one of the following types of diagram: pie chart, bar chart, comparative bar chart, dual bar chart, stem-and-leaf diagram, frequency table. Ask the student to give the advantages and disadvantages of using this type of diagram, chart or graph to display data. Repeat for as many diagrams as time allows.

HOMEWORK ACTIVITY

- **Media search; 40 minutes; page 231**
  Full instructions are given on the activity sheet.

SUPPORT IDEAS

- **Displaying data** For the frequency table, provide the groupings $1 < h \leq 3$, $3 < h \leq 5$, $5 < h \leq 7$, $7 < h \leq 9$, $9 < h \leq 11$.
- **Media search** You may wish to provide some graphs, charts and diagrams for the student to discuss.

EXTENSION IDEAS

- **Comparing data** Construct a pie chart to represent the data shown in the two-way table.

PROGRESS AND OBSERVATIONS

MATHS
— HIGHER —

Edexcel

STARTER ACTIVITY: **3.6 KM**

TIMING: **5 MINS**

LEARNING OBJECTIVES

- Calculate fractions or percentages of whole numbers

EQUIPMENT

1. Next to each percentage and fraction, write that amount of the total, 3.6 km.

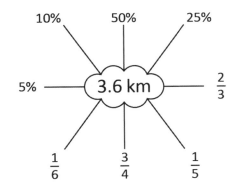

MAIN ACTIVITY: DISPLAYING DATA

TIMING: 20 MINS

LEARNING OBJECTIVES

- Draw and read tables, charts and graphs for discrete and categorical data

EQUIPMENT

- ruler
- graph paper

1. This partially completed stem-and-leaf diagram shows the height of seedlings planted in two different locations.

Location B		Location A
	1	3 4 4 9
	2	0 0 7
	3	3 6
	4	1 1 5 6
	5	2 4 4 9 9
	6	3 4 4
	7	0 0 9
	8	1
	9	0

Key
Location A: 1|3 means 1.3 cm
Location B: 1|3 means 1.3 cm

The heights of the plants in location B are: 4.3, 9.1, 3.5, 5.5, 6.7, 1.9, 3.3, 4.4, 9.2, 8.3, 8.4, 5.7, 7.3, 8.0, 7.2, 6.4, 5.9, 5.3, 4.9, 5.7, 8.2, 2.3, 4.5, 4.9, 6.9, 4.9

a) Complete the back to back stem-and-leaf diagram.

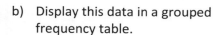

b) Display this data in a grouped frequency table.

Hint: Aim for between four and five groups of equal width. Check that you have included all the data by totalling the frequency. It should add up to 52.

Height (cm)	Frequency

2. Explain why a dual or compound bar chart could be used to display the data, and why this is a good way of displaying the original data. Construct either a dual or compound bar chart to represent the data.

....

....

....

MAIN ACTIVITY: COMPARING DATA

TIMING: 20 MINS

LEARNING OBJECTIVES
- Draw and read tables, charts and graphs for discrete and categorical data

EQUIPMENT
- ruler
- squared paper

1. **Two airlines record the types of meal that passengers order. The information is displayed in the two charts below.**

Airline A (surveyed 1000 people)

Airline B

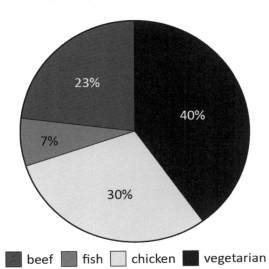

	Vegetarian	Chicken	Fish	Beef
Male	21	43	5	34
Female	29	12	18	38

■ beef ■ fish ☐ chicken ■ vegetarian

Decide if the following statements are true or false. Give reasons for your answers.

a) The number of people who chose vegetarian is the same on both airlines.

b) The proportion of people who chose fish was the same on both airlines.

c) More people chose chicken on Airline B than Airline A.

d) A smaller percentage of people chose beef on Airline A than on Airline B.

e) Write three other true statements about the meals chosen on the airlines.

HOMEWORK ACTIVITY: MEDIA SEARCH   TIMING: 40 MINS

LEARNING OBJECTIVES

- Draw and read tables, charts and graphs for discrete and categorical data

EQUIPMENT

- ruler

Graphs, charts and tables are often used to display data in the media.

1. **Find at least three different examples of graphs, charts or tables in the media. You could look in newspapers, magazines, or on the internet.**

   For each example you find:

   - Decide whether the graph, chart or table has been drawn accurately (for example, if the data is grouped, do all the groups have equal width?).

   - Decide whether you think this is the best way to display the data.

   - Explain any ways in which you think the graph or diagram is misleading.

MATHS
— HIGHER —

Edexcel

36 Answers

STARTER ACTIVITY: 3.6 KM

1. 5% is 0.18; 10% is 0.36; 50% is 1.8; 25% is 0.9; $\frac{1}{6}$ is 0.6; $\frac{3}{4}$ is 2.7; $\frac{1}{5}$ is 0.72; $\frac{2}{3}$ is 2.4

MAIN ACTIVITY: DISPLAYING DATA

1. a)

Location B		Location A
9	1	3 4 4 9
3	2	0 0 7
5 3	3	3 6
9 9 9 5 4 3	4	1 1 5 6
9 7 7 5 3	5	2 4 4 9 9
9 7 4	6	3 4 4
3 2	7	0 0 9
4 3 2 0	8	1
2 1	9	0

Key
Location A: 1|3 means 1.3 cm
Location B: 1|3 means 1.3 cm

b)

Height (cm)	Frequency
$1 \leq h < 3$	9
$3 \leq h < 5$	14
$5 \leq h < 7$	16
$7 \leq h < 9$	10
$9 \leq h < 11$	3

2. So that data for location A and B can be directly compared. Check the student's chart.

MAIN ACTIVITY: COMPARING DATA

1. a) false (A is 40%; B is 25%)   b) false (A is 7%; B is 11.5%)
c) false (A is 300; B is 55)   d) true (A is 36%; B is 23%)
e) Check the student's statements.

HOMEWORK ACTIVITY: MEDIA SEARCH

1. Check the student's work.

232

37 STATISTICS: INTERPRETING DATA

LEARNING OBJECTIVES

- Apply statistics to describe a population
- Interpret tables, charts and diagrams

SPECIFICATION LINKS

- S2, S4, S5

STARTER ACTIVITY

- **What affects averages and spread?; 5 minutes; page 234**
  Challenge the student to explain how to calculate mean, mode, median and range. Explain what an outlier is.
  Then ask the student to follow the instructions on the activity sheet. Encourage the student to explain why the outlier will/will not affect the averages and range.

MAIN ACTIVITIES

- **Calculating from tables, graphs and charts; 20 minutes; page 235**
  Ask the student to work through the questions, finding the measure of location and spread listed.
  Explain to the student that when working with grouped data, the mid-point is used. Establish that this is why the mean is an estimate (since the exact data values are not given).
- **Box plots; 20 minutes; page 236**
  If necessary, remind the student how to find the upper and lower quartiles, and then construct the box plot.

PLENARY ACTIVITY

- **Which numbers?; 5 minutes**
  Tell the student you are thinking of three numbers. The mean of the numbers is 12 and the mode is 15. Ask them to find the range of the numbers. (The numbers are 6, 15 and 15, the range is 9.)
  Challenge the student to design a question like this for you.

HOMEWORK ACTIVITY

- **Revision cards; 30 minutes; page 237**
  Full instructions are given on the activity sheet.

SUPPORT IDEA

- **Calculating from tables, graphs and charts** When working with the frequency tables, you may wish to ask the student to start writing out a list of the data values: 2, 2, 2, 2, 3, ... etc.

EXTENSION IDEA

- **Box plots** Remove the value of 7.3 from the first set of data and ask the student what effect this will have on the box plot. Challenge the student to redo question 2 having removed this value.

PROGRESS AND OBSERVATIONS

STARTER ACTIVITY: WHAT AFFECTS AVERAGES AND SPREAD? TIMING: 5 MINS

LEARNING OBJECTIVES	EQUIPMENT
• Know the advantages and disadvantages of the measures of spread and location	none

1. Explain whether an outlier will affect each of these measures. Give a reason why.

a) mode

----

b) median

----

c) mean

----

d) range

----

e) interquartile range

MAIN ACTIVITY: CALCULATING FROM TABLES, GRAPHS AND CHARTS   TIMING: 20 MINS

LEARNING OBJECTIVES

- Interpret, analyse and compare distributions of data sets from univariate empirical distributions through appropriate measures of central tendency and spread

EQUIPMENT

- calculator

For each of the tables, graphs and charts, calculate the averages and/or range as specified.

1. **This table shows the number of A levels studied by some students.**

   mean = ...   mode = ...

   median = ...   range = ...

Number of A levels studied	Frequency
2	4
3	25
4	31
5	6

2. **This bar chart shows the number of visits made to the doctor per year by 100 patients.**

   mean = ...

   mode = ...

   range = ...

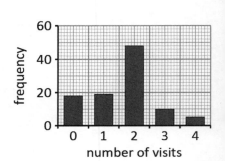

3. **This table shows the age of people using a library.**

   mean = ...

   modal class = ...

   class containing the median = ...

Age (x)	Frequency
$0 < x \le 20$	3
$20 < x \le 40$	14
$40 < x \le 60$	11
$60 < x \le 80$	2

4. **This stem-and-leaf diagram shows the age of people on a train.**

   median = ...

   mode = ...

   range = ...

1	889
2	011356689
3	00558
4	001335899
5	23
6	19

Key
1|8 means 18 years

MATHS
— HIGHER —

Edexcel

MAIN ACTIVITY: BOX PLOTS

TIMING: 20 MINS

LEARNING OBJECTIVES
- Construct box plots
- From a box plot, identify the median, quartiles, range and interquartile range

EQUIPMENT
- ruler
- graph paper

1. **A car manufacturer records the time it takes its cars to accelerate from 0–60 miles per hour on 10 different occasions:**

   5.6   5.7   6.0   7.3   5.8   5.2   5.7   5.9   5.9   5.6   6.2

   a) Draw a box plot for this information on squared paper.

   b) Work out the interquartile range of the data.

   ----

   c) Give one advantage and one disadvantage of displaying the data in a box plot.

   ----

2. **The acceleration time of a different car is shown in the box plot below.**

   5.5   5.8   6.2   6.4   6.6

   Which car would you buy? Explain your answer.

MATHS
— HIGHER —

Edexcel

TUTORS' GUILD

HOMEWORK ACTIVITY: REVISION CARDS

TIMING: 30 MINS

LEARNING OBJECTIVES

- Know the advantages and disadvantages of the measures of spread and location

EQUIPMENT

- index cards

1. **Make a set of four revision cards covering these topics:**

   - mean

   - median

   - mode

   - range

   Make sure you include information on:

   - how to calculate them

   - their advantages and disadvantages

   - how you can calculate them from at least one type of graph, table or chart.

37 Answers

Starter activity: What affects averages and spread?

1. a) mode is unaffected   b) median is unaffected   c) mean is affected
   d) range is affected   e) interquartile range is affected

Main activity: Calculating from tables, graphs and charts

1. mean = 3.6; mode = 4; median = 4; range = 3
2. mean = 1.65; mode = 2; range = 4
3. mean = 38; modal class = $20 < x \le 40$; class containing the median = $20 < x \le 40$
4. median = 35; mode = no mode; range = 51

Main activity: Box plots

1. a)

5.2   5.6   5.8   6.0   7.3

b) 0.4
c) Advantage: The shape of the distribution is easy to see; Disadvantage: Exact values are lost.
2. Either car, as long as the student gives a sensible justification.

Homework activity: Revision cards

1. Check the student's work. Make sure they have included all the required information.

Glossary

Outlier
A data value that sits outside the expected range of the data

38 STATISTICS: SCATTER GRAPHS, CUMULATIVE FREQUENCY GRAPHS AND HISTOGRAMS

LEARNING OBJECTIVES

- Use and interpret scatter graphs of bivariate data
- Construct and interpret cumulative frequency graphs
- Construct and interpret histograms

SPECIFICATION LINKS

- S3, S5, S6

STARTER ACTIVITY

- **Scatter graphs; 5 minutes; page 240**
  Show the student the scatter graph and discuss when scatter graphs are useful (bivariate data). Challenge the student to identify the type of correlation and establish that correlation does not imply causality. Ask the student to draw a line of best fit on the diagram. Discuss extrapolation and interpolation and the reliability of both. Establish which point might be considered an outlier.

MAIN ACTIVITIES

- **Cumulative frequency graphs; 20 minutes; page 241**
  Discuss how to construct a cumulative frequency graph. Ask the student to draw and complete a cumulative frequency column on the table of values, and plot the cumulative frequency graph. Ensure that the student plots the cumulative frequency against the upper bound of the group.

- **Histograms; 20 minutes; page 242**
  Discuss when the use of a histogram is appropriate (grouped continuous data) and establish how to calculate frequency density. Discuss why the frequency density is calculated rather than the frequency, with reference to the example given (widths of groups are not constant). Complete the table of values on the activity sheet, finding the missing frequencies and frequency density. Use the graph to find an estimate for the number of people who attended surgery who were:
  a) over 50   b) under 25
  Discuss why these answers will be estimates.

PLENARY ACTIVITY

- **Scatter graph, cumulative frequency graph or histogram?; 5 minutes**
  Ask the student to explain when they would use each of these types of graph and what data can be read easily from each.

HOMEWORK ACTIVITY

- **All about histograms; 60 minutes; page 243**
  Full instructions are given on the activity sheet.

SUPPORT IDEA

- **Histograms** Provide the axes for the student and model finding the first frequency density.

EXTENSION IDEA

- **Cumulative frequency graphs** Challenge the student to draw a box plot using values read from the cumulative frequency graph.

PROGRESS AND OBSERVATIONS

STARTER ACTIVITY: SCATTER GRAPHS

TIMING: 5 MINS

LEARNING OBJECTIVES

- Use and interpret scatter graphs of bivariate data

EQUIPMENT

- ruler

1. **This scatter graph shows the relationship between the prices of three bed houses and the time taken to travel by train from their locations to London.**

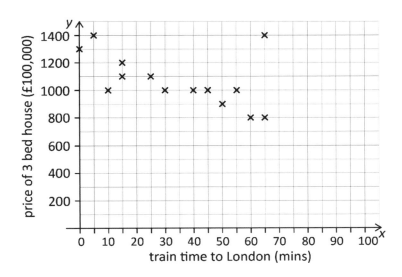

a) What type of correlation is shown here?

----

b) Draw a line of best fit. Which point(s) could be considered outliers?

MAIN ACTIVITY: CUMULATIVE FREQUENCY GRAPHS   TIMING: 20 MINS

LEARNING OBJECTIVES

- Construct and interpret cumulative frequency graphs

EQUIPMENT

- ruler

1. **This table shows the length of time that patients waited for their appointment at a doctors' surgery.**

   a) Draw a cumulative frequency graph to display this information on the graph paper below.

   b) Find the:

Time (minutes)	Frequency
0 < x ≤ 5	5
5 < x ≤ 10	15
10 < x ≤ 15	22
15 < x ≤ 20	7
20 < x ≤ 25	1

   i) median ....

   ii) upper and lower quartiles ....

   iii) interquartile range ....

   c) Use the graph to estimate the percentage of patients who waited:

   i) more than 12 minutes ....

   ii) less than 18 minutes ....

   d) Discuss with your tutor why these answers will all be estimates.

TUTORS GUILD

MAIN ACTIVITY: HISTOGRAMS

TIMING: 20 MINS

LEARNING OBJECTIVES

- Construct and interpret histograms

EQUIPMENT

1. **This table shows the ages of patients who see the doctor one day.**

Age (years)	Frequency	Frequency density
$0 < x \le 10$	7	
$10 < x \le 15$	10	
$15 < x \le 20$		0.4
$20 < x \le 40$	8	
$40 < x \le 60$		1.1
$60 < x \le 70$		0.1

a) Complete the table above.

b) Draw a histogram on the graph paper below to display the information.

HOMEWORK ACTIVITY: ALL ABOUT HISTOGRAMS

TIMING: 60 MINS

LEARNING OBJECTIVES

- Construct and interpret histograms

EQUIPMENT

- filming equipment (optional)

1. **Imagine that you are a Year 11 teacher. Your task is to teach a lesson about histograms. You could record a video or write a plan for what you will teach. Make sure you include:**

   - how to construct a histogram

   - when you might use a histogram

   - how to calculate frequency density

   - how to calculate the frequency if you know the frequency density.

38 ANSWERS

STARTER ACTIVITY: SCATTER GRAPHS

1. a) negative correlation   b) (10,100) and (65, 1400), though answers may vary depending on line of best fit drawn.

MAIN ACTIVITY: CUMULATIVE FREQUENCY GRAPHS

1. a) See graph.
b) i) approximately 12
ii) approximately 14 for upper quartile and 8 for lower quartile
iii) approximately 6
c) i) 44%
ii) 94%
d) We do not know the exact time each person waited as we only have classes.

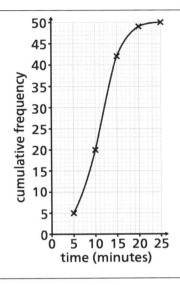

MAIN ACTIVITY: HISTOGRAMS

1. a)

Age (years)	Frequency	Frequency density
$0 < x \leq 10$	7	0.7
$10 < x \leq 15$	10	2
$15 < x \leq 20$	2	0.4
$20 < x \leq 40$	8	0.4
$40 < x \leq 60$	22	1.1
$60 < x \leq 70$	1	0.1

b) See graph.

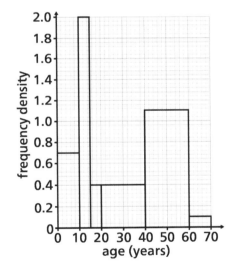

HOMEWORK ACTIVITY: ALL ABOUT HISTOGRAMS

1. Check the student's work. Make sure that all the information has been provided.

GLOSSARY

Correlation
A connection between two sets of values

Extrapolation
Assuming that existing trends continue beyond the limits of data

Outlier
A data value that is distant from other observations

PROGRESS AND OBSERVATIONS

MATHS
— HIGHER —

PROGRESS AND OBSERVATIONS

Published by Pearson Education Limited, 80 Strand, London, WC2R 0RL.

www.pearsonschools.co.uk

Text © Pearson Education Limited 2017
Series consultant: Margaret Reeve
Edited by Elektra Media Ltd
Designed by Andrew Magee
Typeset by Elektra Media Ltd
Produced by Elektra Media Ltd
Original illustrations © Pearson Education Limited 2017
Illustrated by Elektra Media Ltd
Cover design by Andrew Magee
Printed in the UK by Ashford Press Ltd

The right of Catherine Murphy to be identified as author of this work has been asserted by her in accordance with the Copyright, Designs and Patents Act 1988.

First published 2017

20 19 18 17
10 9 8 7 6 5 4 3 2 1

British Library Cataloguing in Publication Data
A catalogue record for this book is available from the British Library

ISBN 9781292195797

Acknowledgements
We would like to thank Tutora for its invaluable help in the development and trialling of this course.

Notes from the publisher
1. While the publishers have made every attempt to ensure that advice on the qualification and its assessment is accurate, the official specification and associated assessment guidance materials are the only authoritative source of information and should always be referred to for definitive guidance.

Pearson examiners have not contributed to any sections in this resource relevant to examination papers for which they have responsibility.

2. Pearson has robust editorial processes, including answer and fact checks, to ensure the accuracy of the content in this publication, and every effort is made to ensure this publication is free of errors. We are, however, only human, and occasionally errors do occur. Pearson is not liable for any misunderstandings that arise as a result of errors in this publication, but it is our priority to ensure that the content is accurate. If you spot an error, please do contact us at resourcescorrections@pearson.com so we can make sure it is corrected.